ELECTRICITY & LIGHTING

HAMLYN PRACTICAL DIY GUIDES

ELECTRICITY & LIGHTING

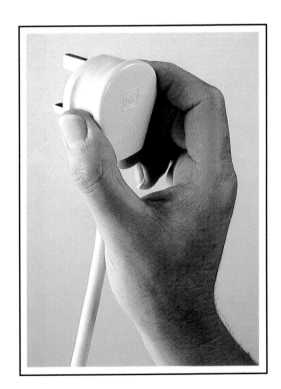

Mike Lawrence

HAMLYN

ACKNOWLEDGEMENTS

Editor:

Lesley McOwan

•

Technical Consultant:

Mike Trier

•

Art Editor:

Pedro Prá Lopez

•

Design:

Edward Pitcher

•

Special Photography:

Jon Bouchier

•

Illustration:

Andrew and Simon Green

•

Picture Research:

Liz Fowler

•

Production Controller:

Jenny May

•

The Publishers thank the following companies and organizations for providing the photographs listed below:
Creda 85 (left); Electricity Council 27 (left); Elizabeth Whiting & Associates 6, 50; G.E.C. 27 (right); M.K. Electric 3; Wickes 86.

For clarity, the earth wires in many of the wiring diagrams are shown as the single colour, green. The actual insulation is coloured with green and yellow bands.

The Publishers thank the following companies for supplying merchandise for special photography:
Besa Lighting Ltd 16, 91; Crabtree Electrical Industries; Consort Equipment Products Ltd; Econa Appliances Ltd 63; Marbourn Ltd; M.K. Electric Ltd; Philips Electronics and Associated Industries 62; Triton plc 84.

All other subjects for special photography supplied by Sainsbury's Homebase.

This edition published in 1990 by
The Hamlyn Publishing Group Limited
a division of
The Octopus Publishing Group
Michelin House
81 Fulham Road
LONDON SW3 6RB

© The Hamlyn Publishing Group Limited
1989

ISBN 0 600 564 649

Produced by Mandarin Offset
Printed and bound in Hong Kong

CONTENTS

INTRODUCTION

Electricity is without a doubt our most useful servant – it's hard to imagine life in the home without it. It gives us light, cooks our food, heats our water and our homes, and lets us use an ever-increasing number of appliances that make household tasks easier and allow us to enjoy our leisure time, all at the flick of a switch. Perhaps because it is so easy to take it for granted, we are also in danger of treating if flippantly . . . or at least, not according it the respect it deserves.

This book is all about doing your own electrical improvements and repairs, and your safety – and that of your family – is by far the most important part of the subject. The actual work involved is not particularly difficult – there is certainly far less skill required than in other popular areas of do-it-yourself such as decorating or plumbing. All you need to do to get first-class results is to exercise care and common sense, and to keep these ten golden rules in mind at all times.

1. Do not attempt to carry out any electrical work unless you know what you are doing and are confident of your ability to carry out every stage of the job correctly and safely.

2. Never work on any part of your home's wiring without first turning off the power at the main on/off switch.

3. If you are working on just one circuit, switch off the circuit breaker protecting that circuit, or remove the fuse if your system has rewirable or cartridge circuit fuses, before restoring the power to the rest of the house.

4. Always double-check all connections inside plugs and wiring accessories, so you can be sure wires go to the right terminals and are properly secured.

5. Remember that water and electricity are a potentially lethal combination. Never touch any fitting or appliance with wet hands, or use electrical equipment out of doors in wet conditions.

6. Always unplug appliances before trying to inspect or repair them.

7. Avoid long trailing flexes (which can be trip hazards) and overloaded adaptors (which can overheat). Both are a sure sign that you need extra socket outlets.

8. Check plugs and wiring connections throughout your wiring system at least once a year for loose connections or signs of wear. Replace damaged plugs and flex immediately.

9. Never omit the earth connection – the only appliances that don't need one are non-metallic light fittings and double-insulated appliances and power tools.

10. Teach children about the dangers of electricity, so that they understand how to use it safely.

KNOW YOUR SYSTEM

If you are planning to carry out any improvement or maintenance work on your home's wiring, it is vital that you understand how the system is put together and how each part works in conjunction with the others. This chapter takes you on a guided tour round a typical domestic installation; use it to find your way round your own home's wiring, which will bear strong similarities to the set-up described here. Doing this now will save a great deal of time and effort when you come to carry out electrical jobs in the future, since you will already have an elementary understanding of how things fit together.

The other thing you must never forget is that electricity can kill. It may kill you if you take chances while carrying out electrical work – by not cutting off the power supply, for example. Worse still, bad workmanship or simple carelessness will put the lives of your family in danger too. Chapter 2 deals with the whole aspect of electrical safety in the home, from official rules and regulations down to plain common sense. Take time to read it carefully, and remember it well.

YOUR POWER SUPPLY

Your electricity supply arrives in your home by either underground or overhead cable. Underground supply is the norm for new properties, but older houses (especially in rural areas) will still have an overhead supply run in from poles by the roadside.

Immediately after it enters the house, the supply cable runs to a sealed block called the service head. This is sited near your electricity meter and contains the electricity board's service fuse, which is designed to stop you taking more current from the system than you should and so overheating and damaging the supply cable. This fuse is usually rated at 80 or 100 amps in new homes, but may be rated at only 60 amps in older properties.

From the service head you will see two thick cables, one black and one red, running to the electricity meter itself. Two similar cables called meter tails run from the meter to what most people refer to as the fusebox – the heart of your wiring system. In modern homes this is a one-piece enclosure housing the system's main on/off switch and the individual fuses for all the circuits in the house. In older homes the on/off switch may be in its own enclosure, and more cables may run from this to separate metal fuse-boxes, one for each circuit. If your system has boxes like this, it may need rewiring and will certainly be difficult to extend – see opposite.

If you have a modern consumer unit, you will see the cables that supply the various circuits in the house running up towards the ceiling and down below the floor. You

Above: Modern installations have a one-piece consumer unit housing fuses or miniature circuit breakers (MCBs) for all the house circuits, and may have a residual current device (RCD) too.

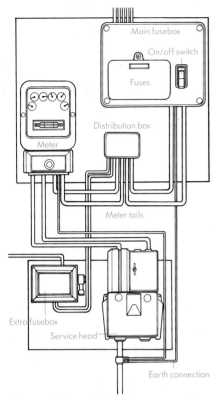

Above: Old installations have several separate fuseboxes, each protected by its own on/off switch and fed by a separate set of tails from the electricity meter. The end result can be chaotic.

If your home is wired to use cheap night-rate electricity (for example, to supply storage heaters), you will have another separate meter and fusebox/consumer unit supplying just the circuits to the heaters (and possibly your immersion heater too).

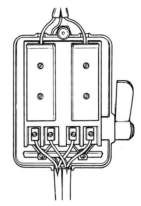

Above: Inside an old fusebox, you are likely to find porcelain fuseholders and cable with fragile rubber insulation which may break down at any time.

Below: Most homes still have systems using (1) rewirable fuses or (2) cartridge fuses. The most modern installations have (3) miniature circuit breakers (MCBs), which are safer and more convenient.

FUSES AND MCBS

Inside the consumer unit, you will find a series of fuses or, on a modern system, small switches called miniature circuit breakers (MCBs). Each of these protects an individual circuit in the house – there will be separate circuits supplying lights, socket outlets and large appliances such as cookers – and each one is rated to suit the demands of the particular circuit. Light circuits, for example, take relatively little current so are rated at 5 amps; power circuits take more, and are generally rated at 30 amps; while cookers may be rated at up to 45 amps. Each fuse or MCB will be either labelled with its current rating or colour-coded for identification.

On modern systems you may also find a separate component called a residual current device (RCD), housed either within the consumer unit or in a separate enclosure beside it. This detects faults in the system and cuts off the current almost instantaneously before it can kill or start a fire.

will also see a green or green-and-yellow cable, somewhat thinner than the meter tails, running from the consumer unit to either a clamp on the incoming supply cable, or to a point beneath the floor where it is attached to a metal rod driven into the ground. This is the system's main earthing cable, and you may also see separate earth cables linking nearby gas or water pipes to the clamp or rod. These are cross-bonding cables; their importance will be explained later – see page 37.

On an older system with separate fuseboxes, each will be linked to the main on/off switch by a length of cable, and each individual circuit cable will run up or down from the fusebox to its final destination. If these cables have rubber sheathing rather than the familiar grey or white plastic covering found on modern cables, they may be unsafe and should be tested immediately by a qualified electrician.

BASIC CIRCUITS

Knowing how electricity works makes understanding your wiring system a lot easier. In a sense, electricity flows between two points, like water through a pipe. Water can provide the power to make things work: to turn a waterwheel or a turbine, for example. So does electricity, creating light (and heat) when it passes through a lamp, or rotation which can drive an appliance if it passes through an electric motor. In each case, what causes the flow is a difference in pressure between the two points; the greater the pressure, the greater the flow.

Electricity can provide power only if it has a circuit to flow round. Within your home, this circuit starts at the incoming supply cable, which

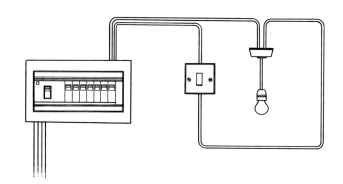

Left: *Every electrical circuit provides a continuous path for the current to flow round. The flow is tapped at various points to allow the current to provide power to lights or appliances, and is controlled by switches.*

body to earth, giving you a shock (or even killing you). This is why every part of your home's wiring system is connected to earth, so that 'leaking' current can flow away safely if anything goes wrong.

Lighting circuits

Your home's lighting circuits are wired up as radial circuits. This

means that the circuit cable starts at its fuse or MCB in your fusebox or consumer unit, then runs to each lighting point in turn before terminating at the most remote one. Most houses have at least two lighting circuits; generally, one serves the ground floor and one the first floor, although you may find some lights not on the circuit you would expect

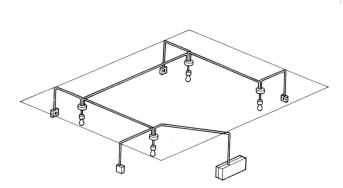

Left: *On a loop-in lighting circuit, the circuit cable originates at a 5-amp fuseway in the consumer unit and runs to each lighting point in turn. The switch controlling each light is wired to its lighting point. Each rose contains three cables, except for the last, which has only two cables.*

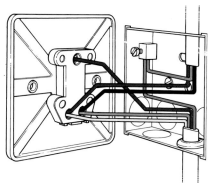

Above: *Within a two-way switch, the switch cable cores are connected as shown. In one-way switches there is no L2 terminal.*

contains two conducting wires or cores. Think of the flow of electricity as entering the house via one conductor – called the 'live' core – and leaving the house via the other – the 'neutral' or phase core. The circuit is completed at your local electricity sub-station. Each individual circuit within your house is tapped off the incoming live supply, and then reconnected to the returning neutral core of the supply cable when it has done its work.

The other thing you need to understand about electricity is that it can escape from its circuit rather like water from a burst pipe. For example, if you touch a live conductor the current passes through your

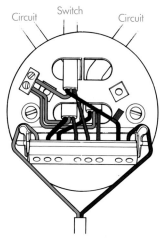

Above: *Intermediate roses on loop-in circuits have three cables: incoming and outgoing circuit cables plus a switch cable.*

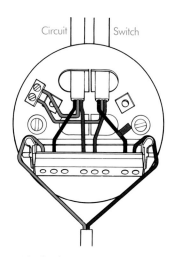

Above: *The last rose on the circuit contains just two cables – the incoming circuit cable and the switch cable for that rose.*

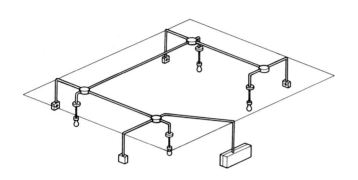

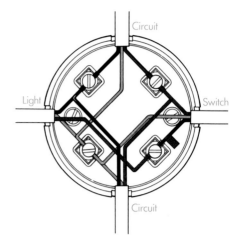

Left: On a junction-box circuit, the circuit cable runs from one box to the next, terminating at the most remote box. At each box, cables are connected to the terminals to supply the lighting point and the switch that controls it.

because it was more convenient to wire the system in that way. Each circuit is protected by a 5-amp fuse.

Circuit types

Lighting circuits are wired up in two different ways, and in most homes a mixture of the two systems is installed to make the most economical use of cable. They are known as the loop-in and junction-box systems.

Loop-in circuits These are wired up, as the name implies, with the circuit cable looping from one lighting point to the next, and the switch cable controlling each light is wired directly into the ceiling rose or light fitting as shown in the diagram opposite. The last rose or fitting on the circuit has two cables – the circuit cable and the cable leading to its switch. All the others have three cables – the switch cable for that fitting, plus the incoming and outgoing circuit cables.

Roses on loop-in circuits have three sets of terminals inside. The live cores on the circuit and switch cables are all connected to the centre bank of terminals. The neutral cores of the circuit cables go to one of the outside terminals, as does the neutral core of the flex to the pendant lampholder or light fitting. The neutral core of the switch cable is connected to the other outside terminal, as is the live flex core, so that operating the switch breaks the flow of current to the light but does not interrupt the supply to the next rose in the circuit. There is a separate fourth terminal to which the earth cores of both cables are connected.

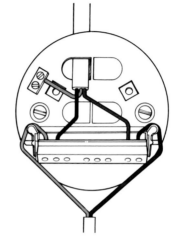

Junction-box circuits These are wired up using extra components called junction boxes. The circuit cable runs from one box to the next, terminating at the last box on the circuit. At each box, two cables are connected into the circuit; one runs to the light itself, the other to the switch controlling it. The last box on the circuit therefore contains three cables, while all the others have four. Each box contains four terminals, wired up in the same way as a loop-in rose: the circuit and switch cable live cores to the first terminal, the switch neutral and light cable live cores to the second terminal, the

Above: Within a four-terminal junction box the connections are made as shown. There is no outgoing circuit cable from the last box on the circuit.

Left: On junction-box circuits, there is only one cable at each rose (unless other lights are controlled from the same switch).

remaining neutrals to the third and the earths to the fourth.

Roses on modern junction-box circuits are usually identical to those used on loop-in circuits, but contain only one cable unless another fitting controlled by the same switch has been linked to it.

Both loop-in and junction-box circuits may have spurs – branch lines, if you like – connected to them, often to feed lighting points remote from the main circuit route. The spur is usually connected to the circuit cable at a three-terminal junction box, within which all live cores go to one terminal, all neutrals to the second and all earths to the third. On loop-in circuits, spurs may also be connected at an existing loop-in rose somewhere along the circuit. Such a rose contains four cables.

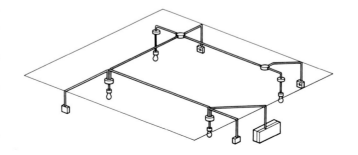

Left: In many homes a mixture of loop-in and junction-box wiring is used, in order to make the most economical use of cable. Spurs may also be wired from the circuits to feed remote lights.

POWER CIRCUITS

Within your home, power circuits supply current to a number of points where you can connect portable appliances such as televisions, kettles and hairdriers to the mains. These are properly called socket outlets, but a great many people call them power points. Each consists of a carefully designed set of recessed terminals into which you push a plug to make the electrical connection. Socket outlets have one, two or occasionally three sockets, and may be fitted with on/off switches and neon indicators.

Modern socket outlets have sockets with three rectangular openings in the faceplate, and are designed to accept three-pin plugs with rectangular pins.

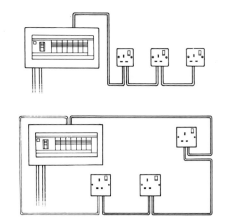

Above: *Modern radial circuits are wired in a straight line, like lighting circuits, while ring circuits form a complete circle.*

Below: *On a ring circuit, the circuit cable runs from socket outlet to socket outlet before returning to the consumer unit. Spurs may be connected via sockets or junction boxes.*

economy of wiring. The only restrictions imposed by the wiring regulations are that each ring circuit should serve a floor area not exceeding 100sq m (1075sq ft), and that the number of spurs should not exceed the number of socket outlets on the ring itself. Ring circuits are wired in 2.5mm² cable and are protected by a 30-amp fuse or MCB.

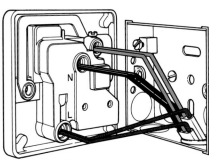

Above: *A socket outlet on the main ring circuit has two cables. The cores should be twisted together in pairs as shown, or may be uncut and crimped into a U-shape.*

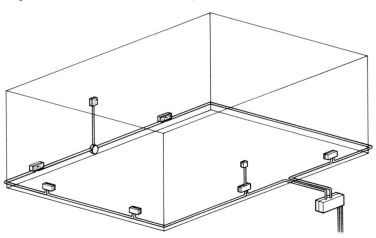

Each plug contains a small cartridge fuse, which is designed to cut off the current to the appliance if a fault develops within it. Two fuse ratings are commonly used in fused plugs: a 3-amp fuse (colour-coded red) for appliances consuming up to 720 watts of power, and a 13-amp fuse (colour-coded brown) for more powerful appliances. Every electrical appliance has a plate or panel on its body stating how much power it uses, so selecting the correct fuse is easy.

Modern power circuits supplying socket outlets are wired up in one of two ways – as ring circuits, or as radials (like lighting circuits).

Ring circuits

As the name implies, these are wired in a ring rather than a straight line; at the consumer unit, both ends of the circuit cable's live core are connected to the fuseway protecting the circuit. This means that current can flow round the circuit in either direction, effectively increasing the circuit's current-carrying ability without the need for heavy-duty cables. Since it is highly unlikely that every outlet on the circuit will be in use at once, there is no limit to the number of outlets the circuit can supply, whether they are on the main circuit itself or attached to it via spur cables (see opposite) for

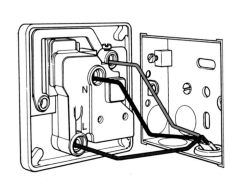

Above: *A socket outlet supplied as a spur has just one cable. Wiring regulations stipulate that spurs may feed only one single or double socket outlet or one FCU.*

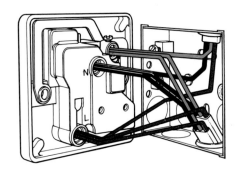

Above: *Spur cables can be connected directly to the ring at a socket on the main circuit. There are three cables at such a socket, which can supply only one spur.*

Radial circuits

These are wired up in a similar way to lighting circuits, with the circuit cable running from one socket outlet to the next and terminating at the most remote socket outlet on the circuit. They are used as an alternative to ring circuits where they offer more economical use of cable.

Radial circuits in modern installations use the same socket outlets as ring circuits, but may be wired up in one of two ways. If 2.5mm² cable is used, the circuit is protected by a 20-amp fuse or MCB in the consumer unit and is restricted to serving a floor area of 20sq m (215sq ft). If 4mm² cable is used, the circuit must be protected by either a high breaking capacity (HBC) cartridge fuse or an MCB (but *not* by a rewirable fuse) rated at 30 or 32 amps; the floor area served by the circuit must not exceed 50sq m (540sq ft). As with ring circuits, there is no restriction on the number of socket outlets on the circuit, and spurs may be supplied so long as their number does not exceed the number of socket outlets on the circuit itself.

Old radial circuits On older systems, you may find socket outlets with round openings instead of rectangular ones. These accept plugs with round pins, and should be regarded as obsolete unless tests show them to be safe to use.

Such circuits were wired up as radial circuits and each was usually supplied from an individual fusebox. Socket outlets and circuit cables of three different sizes were used, according to the type of appliance that would be plugged into it. The smallest was rated at 2 amps, and was intended to supply items such as table and standard lamps. Plugs had either two or three pins (the former had no earth pin). Next in size was the 5-amp socket outlet and plug, with slightly larger pins, intended for small appliances without heating elements such as radios and vacuum cleaners. Lastly, the 15-amp plug and socket outlet had the largest pins and supplied the most powerful appliances such as electric fires,

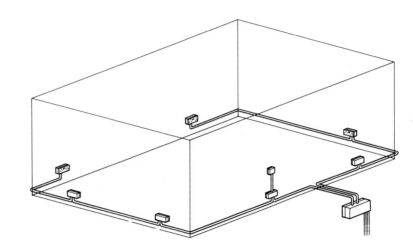

Above: On a radial circuit, the cable runs from socket outlet to socket outlet before terminating at the most remote socket. Spurs may be connected as for ring circuits at socket or junction boxes.

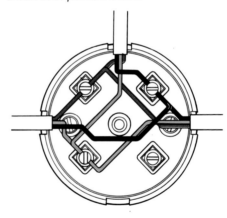

Above: Spur cables can also be connected to ring or radial circuits at convenient points using 30-amp three-terminal junction boxes. Cable cores are linked like to like as shown here.

kettles and washing machines. The plugs themselves were not fused. Instead, circuit protection was provided solely by a rewirable fuse in the circuit fusebox.

Spurs on power circuits

As already mentioned, sockets may be connected to modern ring and radial circuits via spur cables. Such spurs may be connected to the circuit at sockets on the main circuit, or by using a three-terminal junction box cut into the circuit cable at a convenient point. The junction box must be rated at 30 amps, and is wired as shown above. The spur

must feed only one socket outlet (single or double) or one fused connection unit.

Fused connection units

The socket outlet provides the most convenient way of connecting many appliances to the mains, but for certain appliances – such as freezers, waste disposal units and extractor fans – a permanent connection that cannot be unplugged accidentally is more satisfactory. Fused connection units (FCUs) provide this permanent connection; the appliance flex is connected directly into the unit, which contains a cartridge fuse of the correct rating for the appliance. The connection unit may also feature an on/off switch and neon indicator.

FCUs are also available in versions providing a cable connection rather than a flex one, which is useful for wiring remote appliances.

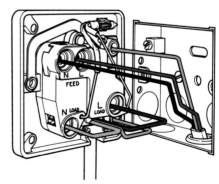

Above: Switched fused connection units (FCUs) provide a permanent connection to the mains for appliances that need a constant, uninterrupted power supply.

CIRCUITS TO APPLIANCES

Apart from the various circuits supplying socket outlets, the modern home is also likely to have circuits and sub-circuits to a surprisingly large number of fixed appliances as well.

Cooker circuits

Small cookers – the sort used in bedsitters, for example – draw relatively small currents, and so can be connected to a socket outlet or fused connection unit on a ring or radial circuit, just like any other appliance. However, a full-sized cooker with oven, grill and several hotplates needs its own circuit, run directly from a fuseway in the consumer unit. The circuit cable runs to a point near the cooker; here it is connected to a control switch which must be within reach of the cooker – wiring regulations stipulate a maximum distance of 2m (6ft 6in). Selecting the size of cable used, and the rating of the circuit fuse protecting it, is described on page 82.

The switch is a special double-pole (DP) type which disconnects both the live and neutral cores of the supply cable. It may also be combined with a 13-amp socket outlet. One double-pole cooker switch of the appropriate current rating can supply a separate oven and hob so long as they are in the same room and are both within 2m (6ft 6in) of it.

From the cooker switch, cable of the same rating is then run to a special connector box on the wall behind the cooker. From there another length of the same cable runs to the cooker itself.

In theory a large cooker with oven, grill and four hotplates could consume as much as 50 amps, which would require a very large (and expensive) circuit cable. However, in practice you are unlikely to be using everything at once, or at their maximum heat settings. So to work out the size of cable you need to supply a cooker, you use a principle called diversity. How this works is explained in detail on page 82.

Below: Basic circuit layouts for wiring to electric cookers, instantaneous showers, wall-mounted heaters in rooms other than bathrooms, and night storage heaters.

Instantaneous showers

Electric showers, like cookers, take high currents – most are rated at 7 or 8kW – so need separate circuits run from an individual fuseway in the consumer unit. Showers rated at up to 7kW will generally need a circuit run in 6mm^2 cable and protected by a 30-amp fuse or MCB; larger types may need 10mm^2 cable and a 40- or 45-amp fuse or MCB. See page 84 for more details.

As with cookers, a double-pole switch of the appropriate rating must be incorporated in the circuit close to the shower heater, and this must be a ceiling-mounted cord-operated switch if it is within reach of the shower – in other words, within 2m (6ft 6in) of it. Alternatively, a wall-mounted rocker switch can be used. In either case, the switch should incorporate a neon indicator to show whether the power supply to the unit is on or off.

Towel rails and wall heaters

Electric towel rails and wall heaters are usually supplied via fused spurs on ring or radial circuits. With towel rails that are within reach of a

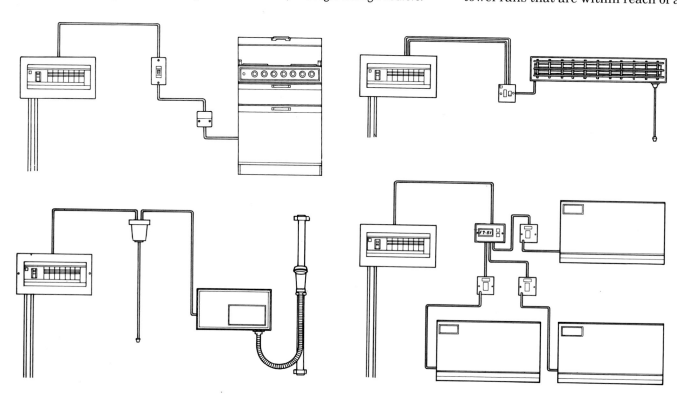

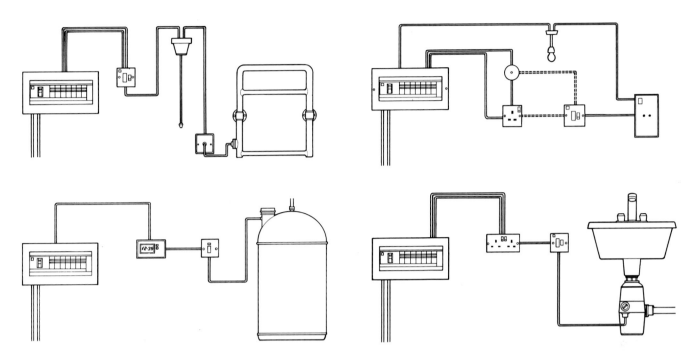

bath or shower, use either an un-switched FCU outside the bathroom linked to a ceiling-operated double-pole switch inside it, or else a switched FCU outside the room. In either case, cable is run from the control switch to a flex outlet plate next to the heater.

With wall-mounted heaters that have their own built-in DP switch, simply run the spur cable to an unswitched FCU and on to the heater. If the heater does not have an integral switch, use the same arrangements as for towel rails.

Storage heaters

Electric storage heaters are available in a range of sizes, with output ratings from 1.7 to 3.5kW. They are wired up on individual radial circuits, each originating at its own fuseway in a separate consumer unit that runs on Economy 7 night-rate electricity. Each circuit is wired in 2.5mm² cable and is protected by a 20-amp fuse or MCB. Each individual circuit cable runs to a 20-amp DP switch near the heater, which is connected to it by a length of three-core heat-resistant flex.

Older storage heaters, no longer available, also often incorporated a fan which provided a means of circu-

Above: Circuit layouts for wiring to towel rails in bathrooms, to immersion heaters, to shaver points and to waste disposal units. Dotted lines indicate possible options.

lating air over the storage elements during the day. The fan was wired up to a fused connection unit linked to a nearby ring or radial circuit to allow it to be operated during the day.

Immersion heaters

Immersion heaters are sometimes simply plugged into a socket outlet, but this is far from satisfactory because of the amount of current such a heater draws. It is better to provide immersion heaters with their own separate circuits, run from the consumer unit.

For a typical 3kW heater, the circuit should be run in 2.5mm² cable and should be protected by a 15-amp fuse or MCB. The cable runs to a suitably rated double-pole switch close to the hot water cylinder; from here the rest of the circuit is run in heat-resistant three-core flex. The switch should have a neon indicator to show when the heater is on. The heater can also be controlled by a time switch, which is wired into the circuit on the consumer unit side of the DP switch.

Shaver points

In bathrooms, you must install a shaver supply unit made to British Standard BS3052. This contains a transformer that isolates the shaver from the mains, and also a current-limiting device that cuts off the supply if anyone tries to plug other more powerful appliances into it. Since the unit takes very little current, it can be connected directly to a nearby lighting circuit, or via a fused spur (fitted with a 3-amp fuse) from a power circuit.

In other rooms, a shaver socket outlet can be used, again wired either directly from a lighting circuit, or via a fused spur.

Other appliances

For many appliances such as freezers, waste disposal units and extractor fans, it is preferable to have a permanent connection to the mains, rather than to use a plug and socket. Here the fused connection unit is ideal; it is simply wired into a ring or radial circuit in the same way as a socket outlet, and the appliance flex is connected directly to it. Use the switched type with a neon indicator to show whether the power is on, and fit a fuse appropriate to the appliance's wattage.

OUTDOOR CIRCUITS

Electricity can be used to advantage outdoors as much as it is inside the house. You can use it to power labour-saving garden tools and equipment, to provide lighting for security or pleasure purposes, or even to create your own water garden with fountains and cascades. You can also enjoy the benefits of having a power supply to your garage, garden workshop, summerhouse or greenhouse.

The most important thing to remember when using electricity outdoors is that the garden is a much more dangerous environment than the house, and the risk of electrocution is greater there than indoors. For this reason it is essential that any wiring work done in the garden should be carried out with the greatest possible care and to the highest possible standard. If you are planning to do any wiring work outdoors and are uncertain of your ability to do the work properly, always entrust it to a qualified electrician. Never take a chance with electricity. Note too that all socket outlets used to power appliances out of doors must be protected by a residual current device to protect the user from shocks.

Outside lights

Lights mounted on the outside wall of the home are wired up as extensions of existing indoor wiring circuits – see page 90 for more details. Lights remote from the house, however, must be wired on their own circuit, run from a spare fuseway at the consumer unit. Ideally the circuit cable should be buried underground where it cannot be damaged, but the cable *can* be surface-mounted on walls if there is a direct route between house and light, or can be carried on overhead poles. It must *not* be run along fences, which can be blown down, or through hedges. Ordinary PVC-sheathed cable can be used so long as it is protected in high-impact PVC conduit. Alternatively, mineral-insulated copper-sheathed (MICS) or armoured cable can be laid directly in the ground – see page 88 for more details.

The circuit wiring closely resembles that for indoor lighting circuits, with the cable looping from one fitting to the next. The main difference is that in most cases the entire run of lights is controlled from just one switch, whereas indoors each light is usually switched individually.

All light fittings used out of doors must be approved for exterior use, and care must be taken with the installation to ensure that all electrical connections are completely watertight. For added safety, it is sensible to provide the circuit with the protection of a residual current device, so that if a fault develops the electricity supply will be cut off immediately.

Low-voltage lighting If you feel that the work involved in installing outdoor lighting is too much trouble, there is an alternative – low-voltage lighting. This is powered by a transformer which is positioned inside the house or within an outbuilding and takes its power from a conveniently-placed socket outlet or FCU. The transformer steps down mains voltage to a perfectly safe 12 or 24 volts, and low-voltage cable carries the current to individual light fittings.

Because the system operates at safe voltages, the circuit cables need not be buried but can be left lying on the surface of flowerbeds, or can be clipped to walls or fences. The spe-

Left: *Low-voltage lighting kits are an easy way of installing outside lights without having to worry about running mains-voltage cables. A typical kit contains two or four lights, complete with ground spikes, a length of low-voltage cable to which the lights are connected directly, and a transformer.*

cial low-voltage fittings can be mounted on wall brackets, attached to trees or positioned on spikes on lawns or in flowerbeds. A range of lamp types is available, with plain or coloured diffusers, enabling you to create a wide range of lighting effects. Furthermore, low-voltage lighting is much cheaper to run than mains-voltage fittings. See page 91 for more details.

Power circuits

Socket outlets can be mounted on the outside wall of your home and wired up as spurs from the power circuits indoors, in much the same way as wall-mounted exterior lights. The socket outlets themselves must of course be weatherproof, and the spur to the socket must be protected by a residual current device situated between the new socket and the point where the spur joins the main current inside.

Outdoor sockets that are remote from the house – used to power tools such as lawnmowers and hedgetrimmers, for example – must be installed on their own circuit, run from a separate fuseway in the house consumer unit, and again protected by a residual current device. The socket outlets must be weatherproof unless they are mounted in weatherproof enclosures, when a standard metal-clad socket outlet can be used. The circuit cable should be armoured or MICS cable, as for remote garden light circuits, but PVC-sheathed cable can be used if enclosed in impact-resistant conduit.

Low-voltage supplies As with lighting, you can use low-voltage circuits to take power out of doors. Of course, this will not drive your lawnmower, but it is ideal for applications such as powering a pump in a garden pond where the combination of water and mains voltage could be particularly dangerous. Again, a transformer in the house or an outbuilding brings down the voltage to a safe level, and the low-voltage supply cables can be run on the surface to wherever they are required. The supply can also run lighting in or around the pond.

Circuits to outbuildings

Outbuildings remote from the house should be provided with their own individual sub-circuit, wired from the house, and this will generally involve the installation of a new small consumer unit or switchfuse unit next to the main consumer unit or fusebox in the house. The power supply to the outbuilding may run underground or overhead, and will terminate within the outbuilding at a second switchfuse unit. This in turn distributes power to lights and socket outlets within the outbuilding itself, and allows them to be isolated for repair or maintenance. The switchfuse unit within the house allows the cable run between house and outbuilding to be disconnected when required.

Within the outbuilding itself, the switchfuse unit may contain one or two fuses, depending on the need for separate individual circuits. In the simplest case, a 20-amp fuse will protect a single circuit feeding one or more socket outlets and a lighting sub-circuit supplied from a fused connection unit also on the socket circuit. Where there are two fuses, there will generally be separate power and lighting circuits, with the former protected by a 20-amp fuse and the latter by a 5-amp one.

Note that the wiring regulations now require all socket outlets used to power appliances out of doors to be protected by a residual current device (RCD). Since sockets in outbuildings are likely to be used in this way, you should therefore include an RCD in the circuit.

Below: Low-voltage supplies can be used to provide safe power for pumps and fountains in ponds as well as for above-ground or in-pool lighting. The cables can be run on the surface or under-ground. Transformers must be sited indoors or within weatherproof enclosures.

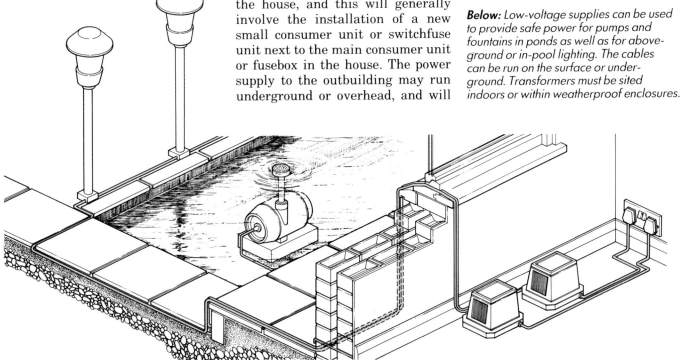

ELECTRICAL SAFETY

Safety is vital not only when you are carrying out electrical work. You and your family use electricity every day, and if any part of your home's wiring system is unsafe, someone in the family could be shocked, burnt or killed. This chapter is all about everyday electrical safety – common-sense safety precautions, plus advice on how to keep your system in good order, simply by carrying out a visual inspection at regular intervals. This gives you a chance to spot problems before they can cause trouble; pages 38-44 describe how to do some of the more straightforward repairs that might be necessary.

Unfortunately, however careful you are, accidents can happen, so this chapter also tells you what to do in the case of electric shock. Study it now, and practise it as often as you can. You never know when you might need to carry the procedures out and save a life.

It is easy to forget that your home's wiring system needs looking after just like any other part of your house. So long as everything works, you tend to forget that it can wear out or develop unseen faults. There are two things you can do to keep it in good condition: the first is to treat it with care and common sense, and the second is to check it regularly so you can spot faults before they become dangerous.

Common sense covers your use of the 'movable' parts of the system – the appliances you plug in and unplug every day, the lights you switch on and off, and so on. These are most at risk from accidental damage. Drop a plug

---

SYSTEMS CHECKLIST
Check the following points regularly:
- Plugs for cracks and loose tops.
- Correct use of plug cord grips.
- Safe connections inside plugs.
- Safe connections inside ceiling roses and lampholders.
- Flexes free from damage.
- Switches and socket outlets securely mounted and undamaged.

EARTHING OF METAL BOXES
Although there are exceptions to the rule, it is generally required that if an electrical fitting (for example, a socket outlet) is mounted on a metal box, an earthing connection should be made between the faceplate and the box. This is done by connecting a short length of cable earth core, enclosed in green/yellow sleeving, between the earth terminal on the faceplate, to which the incoming cable earth core(s) should be connected, and the earth terminal in the box.
(If there is no earth terminal on the faceplate, the incoming cable earth core(s) are connected direct to the earth terminal in the box.)
This regulation ALWAYS applies to fittings with a metal faceplate.

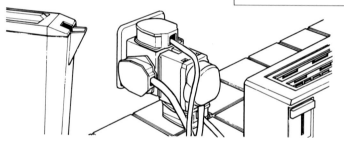

Left: Avoid adaptors if possible, and never use more than one.
Below: Check junction box covers and sleeve bare earth wires.

DOS AND DON'TS

DON'T attempt electrical work unless you know what you are doing and are confident you can carry it out safely.
DO turn off the main system on/off switch before starting any wiring work.
DON'T touch any electrical fitting or appliance with wet hands, and *never* take a portable appliance into the bathroom on an extension lead.
DO unplug appliances before attempting to inspect or repair them.
DON'T omit earth connections on wiring or appliances.
DO double-check connections.
DON'T use long trailing flexes or overload sockets with adaptors.
DO warn children of the dangers of electricity, and protect them by fitting shuttered socket outlets everywhere.

---

on the floor, and you may crack it. Trip over a trailing flex, and you may stretch or break the core conductors, or pull out terminal connections in an appliance or plug. Knock a plateswitch while you are moving furniture, and you may crack its faceplate and expose dangerous live parts. Treat these parts of the system with care, and this type of fault is less likely to develop. If it does, correct it the minute you spot it; delay could cost a life.

Regular checks cover things such as connections within plugs, the condition of flexes supplying pendant lampholders and so on. Frequent use of domestic appliances can cause screw terminals to work loose, while the swaying of a pendant light in a breeze can fray flex insulation or pull out the connections within the rose or lampholder.

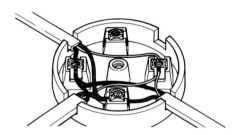

RCD protection

Residual current devices (RCDs) detect certain faults and cut off current almost instantaneously – fast enough to save a life. Make sure you fit one to appliances used outdoors – within a special plug, as an adaptor, within a special socket outlet or protecting the whole house.

FIRST AID

A mild electric shock may give you no more than a tingle in the fingers, but a major one may kill you. If you or anyone in the family receives a shock of any sort from an appliance, stop using it immediately. If the shock is received from a switch or socket outlet, call an electrician to check the circuit.

In cases of severe electric shock, the victim may involuntarily grip the source of the current. Turn off the supply immediately if there is a switch nearby or turn off at the

Below: Never touch a shock victim's flesh. Use a non-conductive object to break the electrical contact.

airway clear. Cool any burns with cold water and cover with a dry sterile dressing. Don't apply ointments to the burn, and don't supply food, drink or cigarettes. Cover with a blanket and call an ambulance.

Lay an unconscious casualty in the standard recovery position, keep the airway clear by tilting the head back and cover with a blanket. *Call an ambulance immediately*, and meanwhile watch for stoppage of breathing or heartbeat. If these occur, give artificial respiration.

1 Clear any obstructions from the mouth with your index finger, then open the airway by tilting the head back and the chin up.

2 Take a deep breath, pinch the nostrils closed, seal your lips over the casualty's mouth and blow (two normal breaths).

3 Watch the casualty's chest rise, remove your mouth, exhale and then repeat the entire process at normal breathing rate.

mains. If not, separate the injured person from the source of the current using a dry object made of a non-conductive material – a wooden broom, for instance. Don't touch the person until they are separated from the current or you will receive a shock too.

Lay the casualty flat on the back with legs slightly raised on a pillow if still conscious but visibly shocked, turn the head to one side to keep the

Right: Lay an unconscious casualty who is breathing in the recovery position and ensure that the airway stays open by tilting the head back and bringing the jaw forward.

THE HARDWARE

Your home's electrical system is like an iceberg; nine tenths of it is hidden from view. What you see on the surface are the various points at which power is drawn off the system to supply light fittings, power points and fixed appliances. Hidden beneath the surface is the skeleton of the system – the network of cables that brings the power from its distribution point at the main fusebox or consumer unit to wherever it is needed.

These cables start their routes at the home's main fusebox or consumer unit, radiating outwards to cross ceilings and floors and run up and down walls, not always where you would expect them to. Where they emerge, they are connected to any one of a wide range of wiring accessories – switches to turn lights and fixed appliances on and off, sockets to allow you to plug portable appliances into the mains, ceiling roses and junction boxes to which light fittings of various types are connected. This chapter takes a look at all the fittings and accessories you may have already or may want to use on your system.

LIGHT SWITCHES

One of the simplest – and most visible – wiring accessories is the humble light switch, or plateswitch as the trade calls it. This is a simple on/off switch – usually operating with a rocker action – which is wired into your lighting circuits to control one or more fixed room lights, and is generally the single-pole type. This means that the switch action breaks only the live side of the circuit. Plateswitches may contain one, two, three, four or even six individual switches, known as gangs. The first three have a faceplate about 85mm (3⅜in) square, while the four- and six-gang switches are rectangular, measuring about 145 × 85mm (5¾ × 3⅜in). They are usually mounted at about shoulder level – typically around 1.4m (4ft 6in) above floor level.

Where wall space is limited, special narrow switches called architrave plateswitches can be used instead. These are just 32mm (1¼in) wide and so can, as their name implies, be mounted on narrow door architraves.

In some circumstances, wall-mounted switches are either inconvenient or unsafe – in bathrooms, for example, where wet hands could cause an electric shock. Here ceiling-mounted switches operated by a pull cord are used instead.

One- and two-way switching

All these switches can be wired up in two different ways, depending on whether they are equipped with two or three terminals on the rear of the faceplate. A switch with just two terminals provides what is known as one-way switching, which means that the lights linked to the switch are controlled only from this switch position. A switch with three terminals can be wired up for two-way switching – in other words, it can be linked to a second switch to allow the light (or lights) to be controlled from either switch. In most homes, the commonest use of two-way switching allows a light on the staircase to be turned on and off from switches in the hall and on the landing. Bedside wall lights switched next to the bed and beside the room door are another example. If more than two switch positions are needed, special intermediate switches (which have four terminals on the back) are used for the extra switch positions.

Dimmer switches

Most switches simply turn lights on and off, but dimmer switches allow you to vary the light's brightness at the turn of a knob. Some have separate on/off switches and brightness controls, but the most common type has a combined rotary switch. With some you turn the knob anti-

Left: (1) Switch with large rocker; **(2)** splash-proof switch; **(3)** ceiling switch; **(4)** standard plateswitches; **(5)** architrave switches; **(6)** dimmers; **(7)** decorative switches.

clockwise to turn the light off, and clockwise to increase the brightness. Others have a push-to-on, push-to-off action, allowing you to leave the brightness at a pre-set level. A few firms also manufacture touch dimmers, which you operate simply by touching the faceplate – briefly to turn the light on or off, and for as long as it takes to alter the brightness to the level required.

Dimmers will operate satisfactorily only between certain defined wattage limits – for example, a minimum of 40 watts and a maximum of 250 watts. It is therefore important to check before you buy a dimmer that it is suitable for the total wattage of the light(s) it will control. Most contain fuse protection to guard against overloading. All should meet the requirements of British Standard BS800 for suppression of radio interference.

Dimmers are widely available in one- and two-gang configurations, and most can be used as part of two-way switching arrangements, using the dimmer as the master control and the other ordinary two-way and intermediate switches as 'slaves'.

Specialist switches

There are several types of light switch available which have additional features.

Time delay switches are among the most useful. They turn a light off automatically after a pre-selected period – anything from two to 15 minutes. They are popular for controlling lights in entrance halls and on stairways, where lights burning unnecessarily can waste money.

Photoelectric switches These incorporate a photocell which turns lights on when it detects a drop in the local light level, and off again when the light level rises. They are particularly useful for controlling outdoor lighting, switching the lights on at dusk and off at dawn (or after a pre-set time lapse if you don't want lights on all night).

Programmable security switches These are used to turn lights on and off at pre-set times to give an empty house the look of being occupied.
Outdoor switches Switches mounted out of doors to control decorative or security lighting must naturally be weatherproof, and are designed to be used in conjunction with PVC conduit. One-way and two-way versions are available.

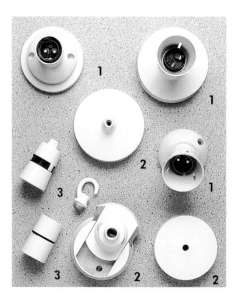

Right: The simplest light fittings are (**1**) batten holders and (**2**) ceiling roses linked with flex to (**3**) pendant lampholders.

Below: Light fittings are available in a wide range of traditional and modern designs to suit every lighting requirement.

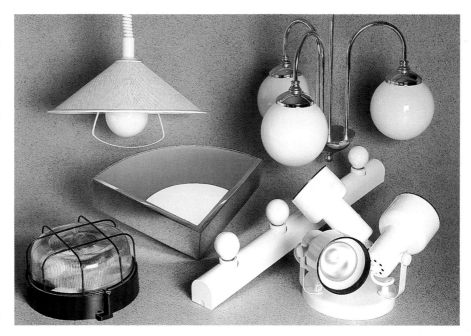

CEILING ROSES AND LAMPHOLDERS

Most modern ceiling roses contain three sets of terminals, allowing the light circuit to be wired up on either the loop-in or junction-box principle. There is a separate earth terminal on the rose baseplate, and there should be small restraining hooks over which the flex cores pass to prevent strain on the terminals.

Pendant lampholders usually contain just two terminals to which the pendant flex live and neutral cores are connected; if they are all plastic, no earth connection is needed. Most are made from heat-resistant materials so they will not become brittle with age, and versions with longer protective shields are made for use in bathrooms.

Batten lampholders are integral fittings that combine the function of rose and lampholder with no flex in between. They tend to be used in utility settings, such as providing a ceiling or wall-mounted light in lofts, garages and so on. They can be wired on the loop-in or junction-box principle.

BULBS AND TUBES

Filament lamps

These come in a wide range of shapes and sizes, from tiny pigmy bulbs to large round globes. For general lighting, the bulb shape may be the traditional pear, the slightly flattened mushroom (ideal for fittings with shallow shades), or the modern squared-off profile. Smaller types such as pigmies and candle lamps with pointed and fluted bulbs are intended for use in smaller fittings such as wall lights, especially where the bulb will be visible. The glass may be clear (used in lamps with reflectors and in chandeliers), pearl (opaque) or coloured.

A variation on the filament lamp is the filament tube, which is used where a bulb would be inappropriate – as strip lighting within cupboards, for example, or in picture lights.

Special bulbs called reflector lamps are used in fittings such as spotlights, and have silvered coatings inside the bulb to reflect light in a particular way. Internally silvered lamps, known as ISL lamps in the trade, have the coating round the stem and sides, and throw light forward, while crown silvered (CSL) lamps have the top of the bulb coated so the light is directed to the reflector in the light fitting itself.

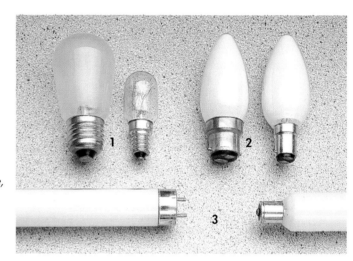

Right: *Filament lamps may have (1) threaded Edison screw caps or (2) bayonet caps. (3) Fluorescent tubes may have bi-pin contacts or single-centre contacts.*

Below: *Lamp types include (1) pigmy, (2) fluorescent bulb, (3) candle, (4) globe, (5) fluorescent tube, (6) GLS, (7) spot, (8) crown-silvered and (9) PAR. Some have coloured glass.*

Parabolic aluminized reflector (PAR) lamps have armoured glass and are used for outdoors.

All these bulbs are described as GLS (General Lighting Service) lamps, and are available in a wide range of wattages. The bulb connects to its lampholder or fitting either via a bayonet cap which is pushed into a spring-loaded socket and turned so it locks in place, or by means of a threaded cap known as an Edison screw cap. Bayonet caps come in two sizes – standard (known as BC) and small (SBC). Edison screw caps come in a wide range of sizes to suit different fittings.

Fluorescent tubes

Standard-sized tubes are 38mm (1½in) in diameter, while slimline tubes are only 26mm (1in) across. Both come in a wide range of lengths. You can also buy miniature tubes, usually 15mm (⅝in) in diameter, for use in smaller fittings. Circular tubes are also available, mainly for use in close-mounted ceiling fittings. There is a range of colours available, with 'warm white' the commonest, but you can also get tubes that give off light to match the yellow light given off by filament lamps. Most have bi-pin end caps which act as contacts and also lock the tube into the fitting, but some smaller tubes have single-centre contacts.

Wattages for standard fluorescent tubes range from around 20 watts

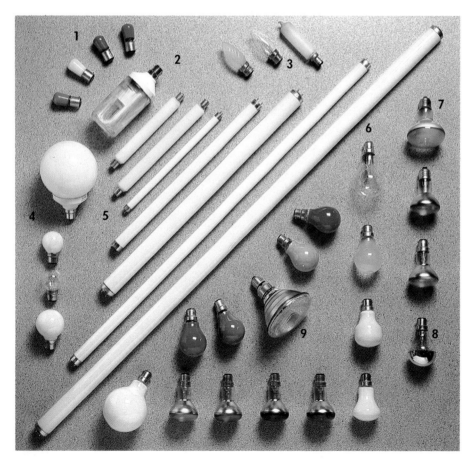

Left: *Socket outlets commonly come in one-gang and two-gang types, although some ranges include three-gang sockets too. Most are switched for convenience and safety, and some include small neon indicators to show when the power is on. Finishes include white and coloured plastic, brass, chrome and enamelled steel. Special sockets with splashproof covers (bottom right) are for outdoor use.*

for a 600mm (2ft) long tube up to 125 watts for the 2.4m (8ft) size. Miniature tubes range from 4 watts upwards.

You can now buy small upright single, twin and triple fluorescent tube fittings designed for use in ordinary lights. They require a small Edison screw or bayonet cap adaptor, and offer the twin advantages over ordinary filament lamps of longer life and reduced energy consumption.

SOCKET OUTLETS

Socket outlets allow you to connect portable appliances, table lamps and so on to the mains supply, by inserting the plug on the appliance flex into specially shaped sockets. Modern circuits have sockets with rectangular holes, designed to take fused 13-amp plugs with flat pins. Older circuits may still have sockets with round holes, for which you need round-pin plugs. These come in three sizes – 2-amp, 5-amp and 15-amp – and were originally unfused; however, you can now buy

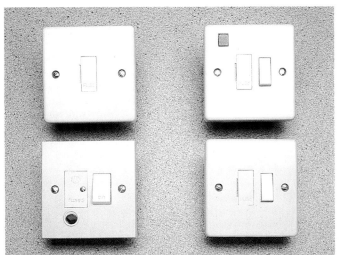

fused versions which offer extra electrical safety.

Thirteen-amp socket outlets are available in single, double and triple sizes, and may be switched or unswitched. The holes should be shuttered for safety, especially if there are children in the family, so that metallic objects cannot be poked into them. The faceplates may also have neon indicators to show whether the

power is on. Sockets taking round-pin plugs are made only as single outlets.

Fused connection units (FCUs) are used to provide a permanent flex connection for large fixed appliances, or to run fused spurs (see page 13). They are available in single versions only, with or without neon indicators, and may be switched (double-pole) or unswitched.

Left: *Fused connection units provide a permanent connection to the mains for appliances such as freezers and washing machines. The fuse fits in a flush holder. The unit may be switched or unswitched, and may have an indicator light. Different types allow flex access from the front or at the edge of the faceplate, or cable from the rear.*

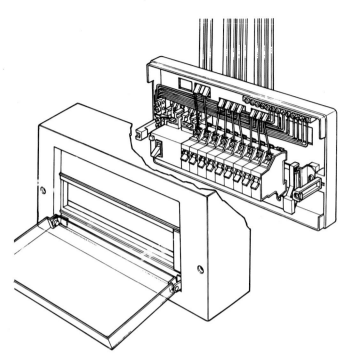

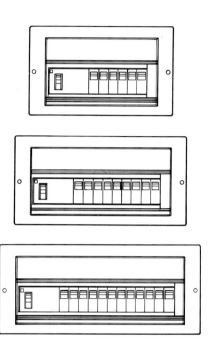

Left: A modern consumer unit contains all the circuit fuses or miniature circuit breakers within a neat one-piece casing, and also houses the system's main on/off switch – or a residual current device if the system is fitted with one. Units may be flush or surface-mounted, and are good-looking enough to be on view.

Right: Consumer units come in various sizes, providing up to twelve separate fuseways.

CONSUMER UNITS

The consumer unit is the heart of a modern wiring system. It contains the main on/off switch and the individual circuit fuseways, and replaces the individual components found on older systems. The circuits may be protected by rewirable or cartridge fuses or, on the most up-to-date installations, by small switches called miniature circuit breakers (MCBs) which offer far better protection against overloading the system than fuses do.

Such units may also incorporate an additional safety device called a residual current device (RCD). This monitors the installation 24 hours a day, and shuts off the power if it detects current leaking to earth – for example, due to faulty insulation which could start a fire, or because someone has touched a live component and received a shock. In the latter case, it will operate quickly enough to save a life. Where an RCD is fitted, it also functions as the system's main on/off switch.

Consumer units are manufactured in a range of sizes, designed to take a number of separate modules – MCBs, an RCD, perhaps a bell

transformer or a time switch to control particular circuits as well. Typically an MCB occupies one module, an RCD two or four, so the size of unit is selected to cope with the number of individual circuits required in the home. Units can be flush- or surface-mounted.

Within the unit, individual circuit fuseways or MCBs are mounted in a line on a heavy-duty conductor called the live busbar, with the highest rated one next to the on/off switch or RCD and those with the lowest ratings – 5-amp light circuit fuses – at the opposite end. Fuses

and MCBs are either marked with their current rating, or are colour-coded: white (5A), blue (15A), yellow (20A), red (30A) and green (45A). The live cores of each circuit cable are then connected to the other end of the fuseway or MCB protecting it, while the neutral and earth cores of all the circuit cables are connected in a group to separate neutral and earth terminals within the unit. Any unused fuseways are usually covered with a blanking-off plate.

If you use cheap-rate electricity at night for space or water heating, you may have either a separate smaller

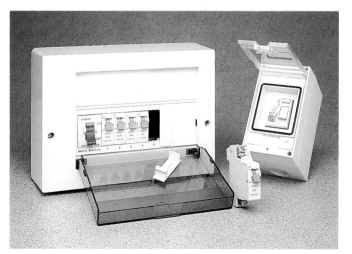

Left: Modern consumer units contain small switches called miniature circuit breakers (MCBs) instead of circuit fuses, and many also have a residual current device (RCD) instead of an on/off switch to provide additional electrical protection. Smaller enclosures are also available (*right*) to allow extra circuits to be wired up.

consumer unit linked to a meter with two registers, one showing consumption at the standard rate and the other cheaper night-rate consumption, or else a larger 'split' consumer unit.

ANCILLARY ITEMS

Apart from the most widely used wiring accessories such as switches, socket outlets and ceiling roses, there are a number of others which may be installed in your home, or which you may want to add to your system.

Double-pole switches

The most important are the special switches used to control large fixed appliances such as cookers, water heaters, electric showers and so on. These are all double-pole switches, isolating the appliance completely from the mains when turned off, and are rated to match the current demand of the appliance concerned; the commonest ratings are 20, 30 and 45 amps. Most are designed for wall mounting, but ceiling-mounted cord-operated switches are also available for use in bathrooms or other places where a wall switch would be inconvenient or potentially dangerous.

Switches are also available with a front flex outlet for appliances such as night storage heaters.

Flex outlets

These are wall-mounted accessories used to link an appliance flex directly to its main supply cable – for example, to connect up an electric towel rail in a bathroom where the switch is ceiling-mounted or located outside the room.

TV/FM radio outlets

These provide aerial connections for

Above: Ancillary items include (**1**) junction boxes, used to link new cables to existing circuits; (**2**) flex outlet plates; (**3**) TV/FM aerial sockets, and (**4**) telephone outlets plus a (**5**) phone cable connector tool.

televisions and/or VHF radios – single and double versions are available, and are linked to loft or rooftop aerials with coaxial cable.

Telephone sockets

These provide outlets in individual rooms, and are a neat flush- or surface mounted alternative to sockets provided with extension kits.

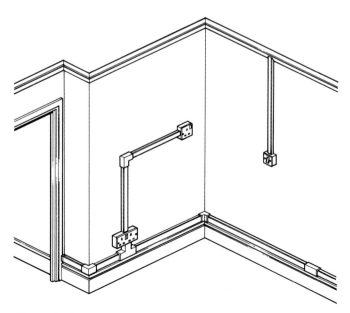

Above: Surface-mounted mini-trunking plus elbows and tees.

Above: Conduit boxes contain connections to light fittings.

PLUGS · ADAPTORS · CABLE AND FLEX · TOOLS

The more mundane but nevertheless vital parts of your system include the plugs, plug-in adaptors and flexible cord (flex for short) used to connect appliances to the mains, and of course the cable with which all the house circuits are wired up.

Plugs and adaptors

On modern power circuits, you will be using three-pin fused 13-amp plugs and adaptors, with 3-amp fuses fitted to plugs on appliances rated at less than 720 watts. It is a good idea to use tough plugs with resilient covers on portable appliances and things like power tools.

If you must use adaptors, never use more than one and double-check that powerful appliances such as heaters do not overload the socket.

Flex and cable

Always use three-core flex unless the appliance concerned is double-insulated – it will feature the double-square symbol – or is of non-metallic construction. Always ensure that cable is of the correct rating for your particular circuit, and that all the bare earth cores are covered within electrical wiring accessories by a length of green-and-yellow PVC sleeving. Never use flex as a substitute for cable in permanent wiring situations.

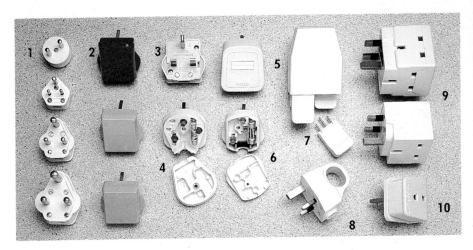

Right: *(1) Round-pin plugs; (2) coloured plugs; (3) 13-amp plug with sleeved pins; (4) safety plug with integral cord grip; (5) plug with resilient cover; (6) plug with cord grip; (7) hi-fi multi-plug; (8) 'easy' plug; (9) adaptors; (10) shaver adaptor.*

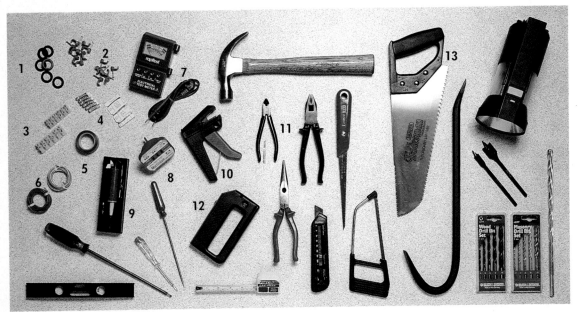

Left: *Specialist accessories and tools for wiring work include (1) grommets for metal mounting boxes, (2) cable clips, (3) connector blocks, (4) fuses and fuse wire, (5) PVC insulating tape, (6) PVC sleeving, (7) a circuit tester, (8) a socket tester, (9) a continuity tester, (10) wire strippers, (11) side cutters and (12) a metal detector. (13) A floorboard saw is useful too. You will also need a selection of general tools – a hammer, screwdrivers, tape measure, pliers, a crowbar, drill bits and a torch.*

Below: *Two-core and earth cable (1-3) in 6.0, 2.5 and 1.0mm² sizes, and 1.0mm² three-core and earth cable (4) for two-way switching.*

Below: *PVC-sheathed flex – three-core (5-7, 9), two-core (8, 10) and fabric-covered (11), plus bell wire (12) and speaker flex (13).*

BASIC TECHNIQUES

Most electrical work involves a series of repetitive actions. For example, you will use virtually the same techniques to wire up a socket outlet and a light switch, and in each case you will have to run cable from A to B and make various connections. This chapter covers each one in detail.

Once you have understood what is involved – and ideally carried out a few practice runs – you will then be equipped to tackle the various projects described later in the book. There you will find that the instructions explain how to carry out a particular project, but do not describe the basic techniques involved, so you may need to refer back to this section from time to time.

READING METERS

Knowing how to read your electricity meter means that you can keep a check on your electricity consumption, spot runaway current usage and also double-check your electricity bill. Modern installations have digital meters just like gas meters, and are easy to read, but many homes have the older-style clock dials recording the units used and these can sometimes be confusing to read accurately.

Start with the left-hand dial, which records units used in 10,000s, and work to the right, recording the readings from the dials marked 1000, 100 and 10 units. Ignore the last dial. Record the digits the pointers have just left on each dial; for example, where the pointer is between 5 and 6, write down 5. Where the pointer is directly on a number, look at the dial on its right. If the pointer on the next dial is between 0 and 1, record the number the previous dial's pointer is on. If it is between 9 and 0, record the number the pointer on the previous dial has last passed.

Above: Older installations may have meters with awkward-to-read clock dials.

Above: Newer homes are fitted with digital meters, which are easier to read.

STRIPPING FLEX

Flex contains two or three conductors, each individually insulated with PVC and enclosed within an outer sheathing. This is most commonly of white or coloured PVC, but special non-kink flexes have a rubber sheath covered with fabric braid. The cores are colour-coded – brown for live, blue for neutral, green-and-yellow for earth. On old appliances you may find these cores coloured red, black and green respectively. Two-core flex has no earth core and is used with double-insulated appliances such as power drills (marked with the double-square symbol), or with non-metallic items like wooden table lamps.

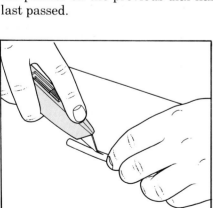

1. To expose the flex cores, slit the sheathing lengthwise with a knife. Do not cut the core insulation.

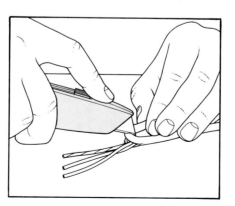

2. Peel back the sheathing and cut it off. If the core insulation is damaged, cut off that section and start again.

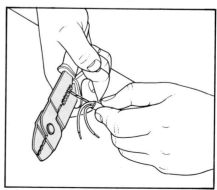

3. Use adjustable wire strippers to remove the insulation after setting the jaw separation to match the core diameter.

WIRING A PLUG

The plug is the all-important link between an electrical appliance and the mains, and must be wired up correctly for safety's sake. This not only entails linking the cores securely to the right terminals, engaging the cord grip securely to prevent tension on the cores and fitting the plug top securely, but also means keeping the plug in good condition. If it is cracked or parts of the casing are missing, it is all too easy to touch

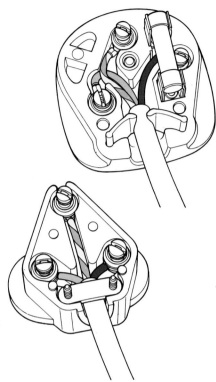

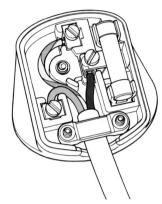

Left: With post terminals a screw secures the core.

Left: With stud terminals the core is held by a washer.

Left: Snap-down terminals hold the core in place.

Above: Most plugs feature a bar-type cord grip which can be inefficient. **Above right:** Jaw-type cord grips clamp the flex as the plug is closed. **Right:** Round-pin plugs do not usually contain a fuse. **Below:** Some easy-to-wire plugs have snap-down terminals.

live parts as the plug is handled, with potentially fatal results. Lastly, the right fuse must be fitted – a red 3-amp one for appliances up to 720 watts, a brown 13-amp one otherwise.

EXTENDING FLEX

Ideally, every electrical appliance should have a continuous flex long enough to reach from appliance to socket, but in many situations you will want a longer flex, when fitting a completely new length to the appliance or using an extension reel will not be a convenient solution. In this case you need to join an extra length of flex to the existing one, and for this you should use a special flex connector.

One-part connectors are ideal for flexes that will stay in one position – supplying a standard lamp, for example. Two-part connectors are better for portable appliances such as vacuum cleaners or powered garden tools, where you do not want to store the extra flex on the appliance. With this type, always connect the part with the pins to the flex running to the appliance.

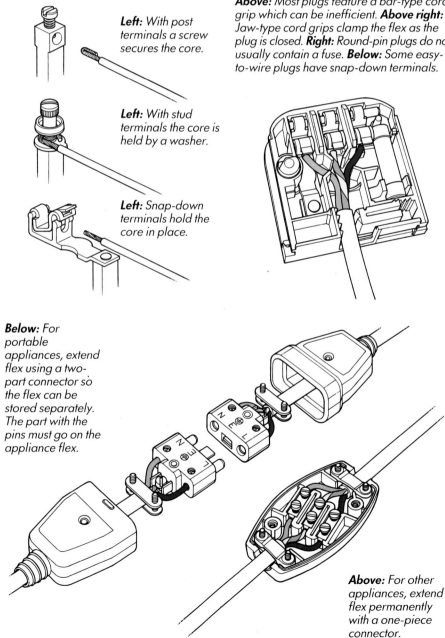

Below: For portable appliances, extend flex using a two-part connector so the flex can be stored separately. The part with the pins must go on the appliance flex.

Above: For other appliances, extend flex permanently with a one-piece connector.

WIRING A PENDANT LIGHT

Flex also connects pendant lampholders to their ceiling roses. Use round PVC-sheathed two-core $0.5mm^2$ flex without an earth, unless the lampholder is metallic, when three-core flex with an earth must be used. For lampshades weighing over 2kg (4½lb), fit $0.75mm^2$ flex instead.

Within the ceiling rose, strip back the insulation on the flex cores to allow them to be connected to the switch live and circuit neutral terminals (see diagram), and loop each core over the support hook to prevent any strain on the connections. At the lampholder, again carefully strip the cores, connect them to the lampholder terminals and loop them over the support hooks. Remember to thread the flex through the rose and lampholder covers *before* making the final connections.

Luminaire support couplers

Several wiring accessory manufacturers make special plug-and-socket connectors that take the place of the conventional ceiling rose. The flex from the pendant lampholder is wired to a specially-designed plug which engages in the ceiling-mounted socket, allowing the light to be taken down when required for cleaning and repair, or when the room is being decorated. The circuit cables are connected to the socket part of the coupler as for a rose.

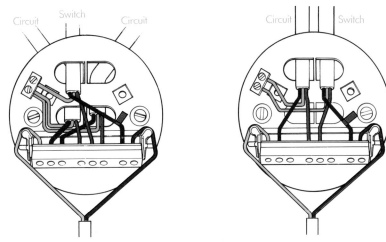

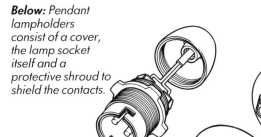

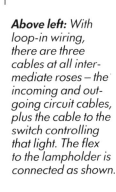

Below: *Pendant lampholders consist of a cover, the lamp socket itself and a protective shroud to shield the contacts.*

Above left: *With loop-in wiring, there are three cables at all intermediate roses – the incoming and outgoing circuit cables, plus the cable to the switch controlling that light. The flex to the lampholder is connected as shown.*

Above: *At the last rose on a loop-in system there are two cables – the main circuit and the switch cable.*

Left: *A luminaire support coupler has a ceiling-mounted socket and cover, into which a special plug carrying the flex and lampholder fits.*

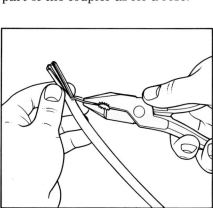

1. To strip cable sheathing, either slit it with a knife or grip the earth core with pliers and pull this to split the PVC.

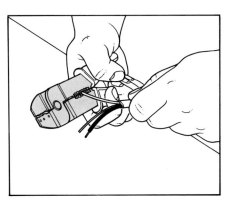

2. Use adjustable wire strippers to remove the core insulation, with the jaw separation matching the core diameter.

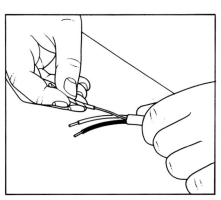

3. Before connecting the cable to a wiring accessory, always cover the bare earth core with sleeving.

PLANNING CABLE RUNS

One of the most awkward and time-consuming techniques involved in electrical wiring work entails getting circuit cables from A to B with the minimum of damage and disruption to furnishings and decorations. In new homes, the circuit cables are run across walls and floors before ceilings are fitted and walls plastered. However, in established properties you are faced with two choices. The first involves running the cable on the surface – either simply clipped into place, or run in some sort of mini-trunking – to wherever it is needed. The second involves lifting floorboards to gain access to the void beneath, and chopping out channels in wall surfaces so the cables can be completely concealed. This is obviously much more disruptive, and appropriate only where you are planning a major revamp of a room.

Apart from deciding how you intend to run your circuit cables when altering or extending your wiring, you also need to plan the exact route it will take. The two decisions are in a sense interdependent; whether you choose surface or flush runs will dictate the cable route to an extent.

With surface mounting, you can simply clip the cable to the wall surface, or to the tops of skirting boards and the sides of door architraves. Never run it unprotected across floors, however, because of the risk that it might be damaged. Use cable clips of the appropriate size, spaced about 200mm (8in) apart. Remember that you can always change the cable run to a concealed installation at a future date when you are preparing to strip the room for complete redecoration.

An alternative to 'bare' surface mounting is to conceal the cable in some sort of trunking. The simplest type is a slim square or rectangular conduit which is pinned, screwed or stuck to the wall surface. You then simply lay in the cable and clip on the cover to conceal it. The smallest size will contain only one cable, but

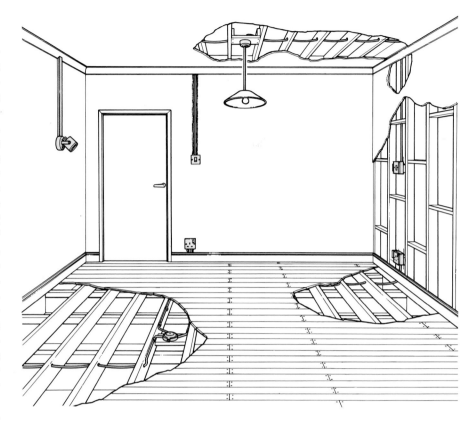

Above: In a typical room you have the choice of surface-mounting cables, or of concealing them above ceilings, underneath floorboards and behind wall surfaces.

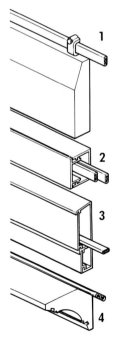

Left: You can surface-mount cable simply by **(1)** running it along the top edges of skirting boards and round door architraves and window frames, using cable clips to hold it in place. Neater alternatives include **(2)** PVC mini-trunking with a snap-on cover, **(3)** skirting and architrave mouldings and even **(4)** decorative cornice. Mini-trunking is available in several sizes; the larger ones will accommodate several cables.

larger sizes can accept several, and there is a comprehensive range of accessories to enable you to run the cable round corners and link it to wiring accessories. Again, you can use trunking on a permanent basis, or until the opportunity arises to

switch to concealed cable runs.

Better still, you can replace existing skirtings and architraves with proprietary plastic mouldings which conceal cable runs and can also hide water supply and central heating pipework. They clip into position once the cable runs have been secured with cable clips.

Wiring accessories

If you decide to run cables on the surface, you may also prefer to surface-mount your wiring accessories such as new switches, sockets and so on. All these accessories can be fitted to surface-mounted plastic backing boxes, with the cable running in through knockouts in the box sides or, in the case of mini-trunking, via special connectors. You can convert them to flush-mounting at a later date if you wish.

CABLE IN SOLID WALLS

Concealing cables beneath the surface of plastered walls is undoubtedly the neatest solution, but does of course involve the most work both during the actual installation and in making good afterwards. Because of the disruption involved, it is best to plan the work to coincide with a major redecoration programme.

Start by marking out on the wall surface the precise route the cable will take. Remember that cables should always run either vertically or horizontally, *never* diagonally. This ensures that anyone making fixings into wall surfaces in the future, or wanting to make further alterations to the existing wiring, knows where to expect cables to be.

Now you can start cutting the channel (called a chase) in which the cable will be run. Aim to make it about 25mm (1in) wide if you will simply plaster over the cable, and around 50mm (2in) wide if you intend to use conduit or protective channelling (see below). The traditional way of doing this is with a sharp brick bolster and a club hammer, but this is a slow and tedious task on all but relatively small jobs. If you have a lot of chasing to do on a large project, it is well worth hiring a specialist power tool called a chasing machine to do the job for you. This has a specially shaped cutter that forms a neat groove in the plaster as you drive it along the cable route. However, it does create a lot of dust, so be prepared for this.

You should aim to cut right back to the brickwork or blockwork behind the plaster. In modern homes the plaster is rarely more than about 13mm (½in) thick, but in older properties it may be as much as 25mm (1in) thick (and very soft and crumbly, so you may have to do more patching up afterwards than you expected). When you have cut out the full length of the chase, use a cold chisel to rake out the remaining debris along the bottom of the chase.

You can now run in the cable. If you intend simply to plaster over it, secure it in place with cable clips spaced about 300mm (12in) apart. However, it is preferable to give the cable some additional protection, and the advantage of using protective channelling or conduit is that you can easily alter or add to the wiring in the future using the same channel for the new cables.

Protective PVC channelling is just a flanged cover strip which you fix to the wall over the cable with masonry pins. Different widths are available to cope with one or more cables. Conduit is a PVC tube which you secure to the base of the chase with galvanized clout nails; unless your chases are deep use the flattened oval type rather than round conduit.

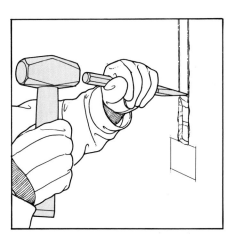

1. To conceal cable in solid walls, first mark the cable position. Then chop out the plaster with a hammer and bolster.

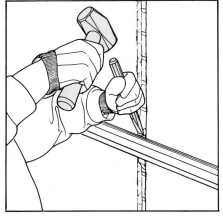

2. If you work carefully, you can cut the plaster out behind picture and dado rails without disturbing them.

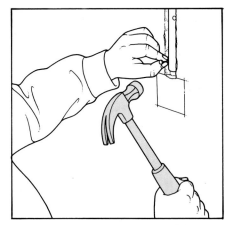

3. You can plaster over the cable run, but it is better to pin lengths of oval or round PVC conduit into place first.

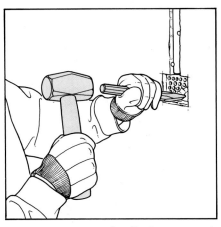

4. To cut recesses for flush-mounted wiring accessories, honeycomb the masonry with drill holes first.

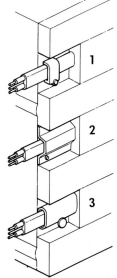

Left: *You can simply secure the cable in the chase with (1) clips and plaster over it. However, using (2) PVC channelling or (3) conduit gives the cable additional protection and also allows you to draw in new or replacement cables along the run in the future.*

CABLE IN STUD WALLS

Most homes have some internal walls built as timber stud partitions, and running cable across these calls for a different technique. Some older homes have solid masonry walls covered with lath-and-plaster on timber battens, so there is a gap behind the plaster. You may also have to take special care with wiring work in a timber-framed house.

With stud partition walls, you have to thread your circuit cables through the void between the plasterboard cladding on each side of the partition. Therefore your first step must be to locate the positions of the vertical studs and any horizontal braces (called noggings) that lie on your proposed cable route. You can find their approximate positions by tapping the wall surface and listening for the dull thud that indicates solid timber behind, or you can use a clever device called a stud finder. This is basically a metal detector that reacts to the lines of nails holding the plasterboard in place.

At each point where the cable run crosses a stud or nogging, cut out a small 'window' in the plasterboard about 75mm (3in) square, using a sharp handyman's knife. Keep the patch you cut out, so you can replace it later. Chisel a groove in the edge of the timber to allow the cable to pass it. If you are running the cable

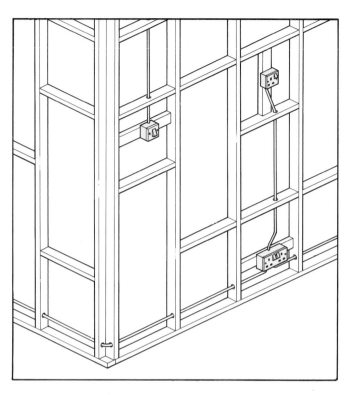

just along the foot of the wall, prise off the skirting board so the cable can be run in the gap between the bottom edge of the plasterboard and the floor.

To feed the cable into the gaps between the studs, you have to bore a hole in the head plate, so you'll need access to the ceiling void above the room where the wall is. Lower a weight on a long piece of string through the hole and fish it out through your 'window' lower down.

Tie the string to the cable and pull on the weighted end to draw the cable through. When you have completed the cable run, simply nail the patches back in place and fill round them to disguise the joins.

Use a similar technique to run cables behind lath-and-plaster walls, cutting windows to expose the vertical support battens for horizontal cable runs. There will not be any horizontal noggings to interfere with vertical cable runs.

Left: If you are building a stud partition wall from scratch, run the wiring in when the timber framework is complete. Drill holes in studs and noggings so you can thread the cables into place, and fit supporting battens to which you can then attach mounting boxes for flush wiring accessories. Make sure the cable holes are in the centre of the timbers, so that the plasterboard fixing nails cannot damage them, and keep all cable runs vertical or horizontal.

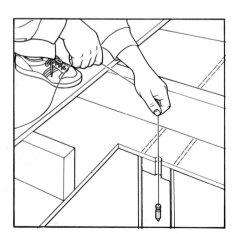

1. To run cable inside a stud wall, drill through the head plate from the room above so you can lower a weighted line.

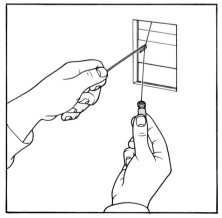

2. Where the line hits a timber nogging, cut a small window out of the plasterboard so you can hook it out.

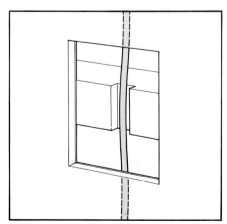

3. Use the line to draw the cable into position, and cut a notch in the nogging with a chisel to allow it to pass.

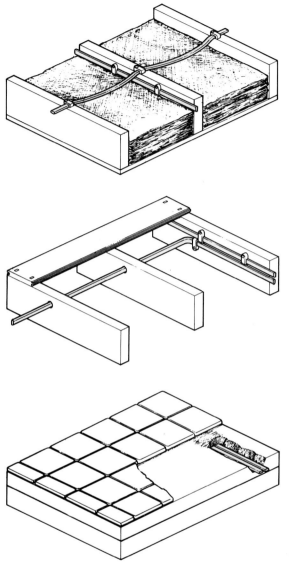

Left: In lofts, clip cables to the sides of joists above any loft insulation where they run parallel to the joist line. Runs across the joint line can be clipped to the top of the joists.

Left: Underneath suspended timber floors, leave cables between joists to rest on ceilings below, or clip them to the joist sides if you have access to the underfloor void. Drill holes in the centre of the joists to allow cables to cross the joist line.

Left: In solid floors, cut a shallow channel in the surface screed and lay the cables in place, ideally inside PVC conduit for added protection. Take care not to damage the damp proof membrane in solid ground floors.

CABLE ACROSS FLOORS AND CEILINGS

Apart from passing up and down wall surfaces, cable runs also need to cross floors and ceilings. The space beneath suspended timber ground floors or between upper floors and ceilings is a perfect place to conceal them. The amount of work involved in running the cables depends on the ease of access, and on whether the cable run crosses or runs parallel to the line of the joists.

Generally the easiest place to work is in the loft, where you have virtually unrestricted access to top-floor ceilings and the head plates of any partition walls in rooms directly below the loft space. You can simply clip cables to the sides of the joists, but where they cross the joist line it is better to bore holes through the centres of the joists than to cut notches in their top edges or to run the cables over them. Notches may weaken the joists, and cables crossing them could be easily damaged.

Ensure that cables are not covered by loft insulation wherever possible, especially if expanded polystyrene foam is present since it can cause deterioration of the cable sheath.

If you have suspended timber ground floors with a crawl space underneath, you can simply clip the cables to the joists. There is no need for holes if cables cross the joists.

For other floor/ceiling voids, you will have to lift floorboards to gain access. Where the cable will run across the joist line, you need lift only one line of boards right across the room. You can then drill holes in the centre of each joist and thread the cable through, leaving a little slack between each pair of joists. As in lofts, it is unwise to cut notches in the top edges of the joists. Apart from the possibility that notches may weaken the joists, it also exposes the cables to the risk of having a floorboard nail driven through them unless you are prepared to go to the trouble of fitting protective metal plates over each notch. Space between the joists may make drilling awkward, but it doesn't matter if the holes are drilled at an angle.

Where the cable runs parallel to the joist line, you will generally be able to feed it through between the joists after first lifting a board at each end of the run. Use a small mirror and a torch to check that there are no obstructions along the proposed cable route. The likeliest problem is to find herringbone strutting fitted between the joists, and you may also have problems with old lath-and-plaster ceilings, since the cable will tend to snag on the plaster nibs as you try to feed it through. In either case, you will have to lift more boards at about 1.2m (4ft) intervals across the room so you can guide the cable across. Otherwise, simply push the cable in at one end of the run and draw it out at the other, leaving it lying loose on the surface of the ceiling below.

Solid floors

Where you have solid ground floors, the neatest method of running cables across them is to cut a shallow channel in the floor screed. However, you must be careful not to damage the dampproof membrane, which may be close to the surface. You *can* simply mortar over the cable run, but it is better to protect it with flat oval PVC conduit laid in the floor channel.

SURFACE-MOUNTING ACCESSORIES

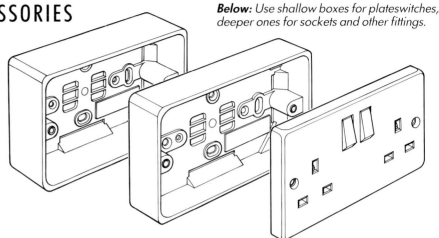

Below: Use shallow boxes for plateswitches, deeper ones for sockets and other fittings.

Surface-mounting is the simplest way of fixing wiring accessories – light switches, socket outlets and so on – to your house walls, since you do not disturb existing decorations. Set against that is the slightly increased risk of damage to the accessory because of the distance by which it projects from the wall surface. The accessory is fixed to a plastic or metal backing box which is in turn screwed to the wall. The cable can be run to the box over the wall surface, along skirtings and up the sides of architraves, and is either clipped in place or concealed with mini-trunking. It enters the box through a knockout – a thin area of plastic or a pre-punched metal disc in the side or base of the box.

On solid walls, the backing box is secured with woodscrews driven into wallplugs, while on stud walls it should be mounted directly over a stud or nogging if possible. Cavity fixings can be used for most accessories where fixing to a supporting timber is not possible but should be avoided for socket outlets because the action of pulling out plugs can weaken the fixings. As a last resort mount them on skirting boards.

With plastic backing boxes, the circuit earth cores should be connected to the earth terminal on the accessory faceplate. With metal boxes, add a short earth core to link the accessory's earth terminal to the earth terminal on the box.

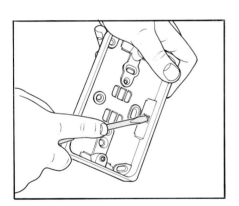

1. Decide where the cable will enter the box, and remove a knockout.

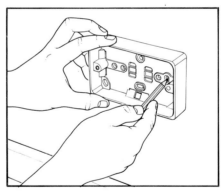

2. Offer the box up to the wall and mark the positions of the fixing screws.

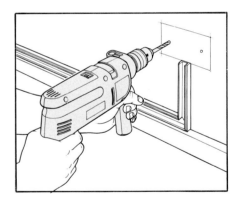

3. Drill and plug the holes, and fit mini-trunking for the cable.

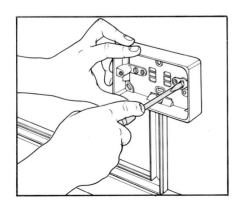

4. Screw the box to the wall, checking that it sits truly level.

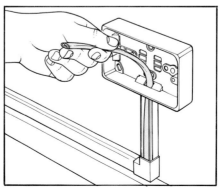

5. Run the cable in via the mini-trunking and through the knockout.

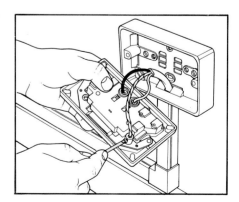

6. Prepare the cores and connect them to the accessory's terminals.

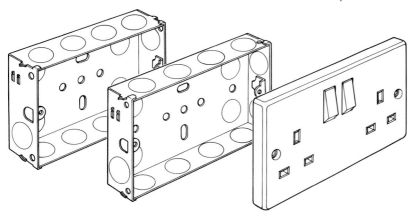

Below: Galvanized steel flush boxes also come in shallow and deep versions.

MOUNTING FLUSH ACCESSORIES

accessory's earth terminal to the earth terminal in the mounting box. the accessory projects from the wall only by the thickness of its faceplate. The galvanized steel box is actually fixed into a recess chopped in the masonry, and the cable usually reaches it via a chase cut in the plaster, entering through a knock-out in the side or back of the box.

If you are using metal accessories, add a sleeved earth core to link the accessory's earth terminal to the earth terminal in the mounting box.

Chopping a recess in the wall can be a tricky job; it is best first to drill a series of holes to the correct depth with a masonry drill, then to cut out the resulting honeycomb of brick or blockwork with a brick bolster and a sharp cold chisel. Care must be taken when chopping holes in cavity walls and internal partitions where the masonry is only about 110mm (4½in) thick, especially for deep-mounted boxes such as those used for cooker controls, since over-zealous hammering may result in a complete breakthrough. In this case, you can use shallower backing boxes and accessories with faceplates that are thicker than usual.

Once the recess has been formed, feed the cable into the backing box through a grommet. Secure the box with screws and wallplugs and make good. Then fit the accessory.

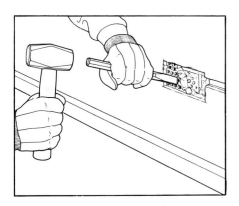

1. Drill holes to honeycomb the masonry and chop out the waste.

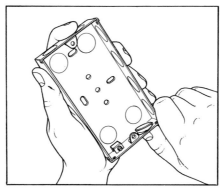

2. Decide where the cable will enter the box, and push out a knockout.

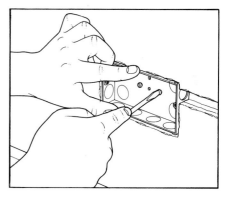

3. Check that the box fits, drill and plug the wall and screw in the box.

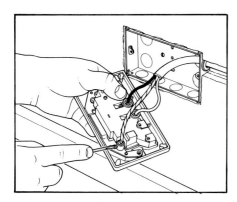

4. Run in the cable, prepare the cores and attach them to the terminals.

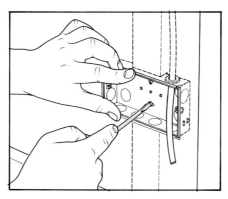

5. On stud partition walls, fit the box to a notch cut in a stud if possible.

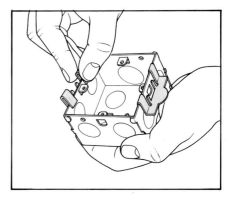

6. Otherwise, use clip-on lugs that will grip the rear face of the plasterboard.

Cavity wall boxes

If you want to flush-mount accessories in stud partition walls, there is an ingenious alternative to the traditional methods of fixing the backing box shown on page 35. It involves making a cut-out in the plasterboard and inserting a special backing box with spring-loaded lugs at each side. (It is of course essential that the hole is cut accurately to size.) As the box is pushed into the hole, the lugs are squeezed inwards; when it is fully home, they spring out to grip the inner face of the plasterboard and provide a firm fixing for the accessory faceplate.

Right: Cavity wall boxes have spring-loaded lugs that grip the rear face of the wallboard.

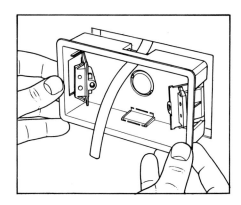

CEILING ACCESSORIES

Fixing wiring accessories to ceilings poses much the same problem as mounting them on stud partition walls: a firm fixing is essential.

For ceiling mounted accessories, it is best to secure the baseplate in place by screwing it directly to a joist. Decide on the fixing position for the accessory, and locate a nearby joist by tapping the ceiling and listening for the dull sound that indicates solid timber. Push a long, thin-bladed screwdriver through the ceiling so you can see the tip after gaining access to the ceiling void from the floor above. Drill a hole in the ceiling and pass the circuit cable down through it, clipping it to the side of the joist. Then go downstairs and screw the accessory backplate to the joist after removing the knock-out to allow the cable through.

If you cannot mount the accessory beneath a joist, you must place a bridging batten between adjacent joists using screwed-on fixing blocks so it rests on the top surface of the ceiling. Drill a hole through the batten and the ceiling, pass through the cable, then secure the baseplate with screws driven through the ceiling into the batten.

Use this batten technique to install recessed conduit (BESA) boxes which accommodate wiring connections to certain types of flush-fitting lights. Do not cut away sections of joist to fit these boxes, as this can weaken the joist. Start by drawing the outline of the box on the ceiling at a point between adjacent joists, then use a padsaw to cut the hole. Fit the batten between the joists – loosely, without fixing screws, and ask someone to hold the box in place in the hole while you mark the correct level of the batten on the joist sides. You should fit it so the lip of the box is just within the edges of the hole. Now secure the batten's fixing blocks to the joist and attach the box to it, ready for the cable to be run in.

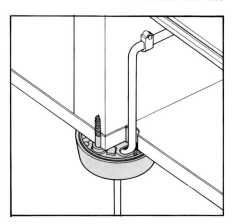

1. If possible, mount ceiling roses and junction boxes directly under a joist.

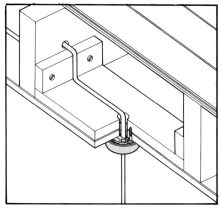

2. Otherwise, secure a batten between the joists and screw the accessory to it.

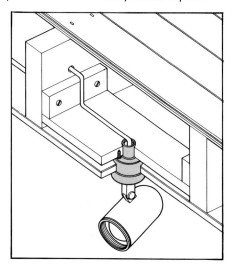

3. For flush-fitting lights, secure a conduit box to a batten as in 2.

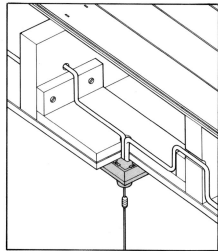

4. Use a batten again to provide a secure fixing for ceiling switches.

USING COAXIAL CABLE

Coaxial cable is used to connect rooftop, loft or portable television and radio aerials to their receivers. The cable itself consists of a solid central core, surrounded by special honeycomb plastic sheathing round which a sleeve of fine mesh screening wires are wrapped. The whole cable is then covered in a flexible plastic outer sheathing. To prepare the cable for connection to its aerial, to an aerial socket outlet or to a connecting plug, start by cutting back the outer sheathing with a sharp knife, taking care not to damage the screening wires inside. For connection to an aerial plug, neatly trim back the braiding by about 6mm (¼in) with sharp scissors or side cutters to leave a neat edge, and slip the plug's screw-on cap over the end of the cable. You then push the cable grip over the cable end and press in its flexible arms so they grip the cable sheathing, and fold the braiding back over it. Finally, slip on the plastic pin moulding followed by the plug body, and push up the plug cap so you can screw the two together. If necessary, trim back the central core so it is flush with the end of the pin moulding.

For connection to aerials and sockets, simply strip the outer sheathing, pull the braiding to one side and solder ring tags to both the braiding and the core conductor.

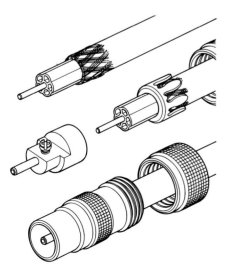

EARTHING AND CROSS-BONDING

Earthing provides a safe escape route for current to flow harmlessly to earth in the event of an electrical fault. The continuity of the home's earthing system is therefore vitally important. Every circuit and wiring accessory is connected to earth by means of the earth continuity conductor (ECC) in each circuit cable. In addition, metal pipework and metallic equipment in rooms where water and electricity are in close proximity – especially taps, metal kitchen sinks and cast-iron or steel baths – are also cross-bonded to earth so that, should they come into contact with a live conductor, the current flows safely to earth and you do not get a shock if you touch it. The various earthing and cross-bonding connections you are likely to find on your wiring system are shown below; they should not be tampered with.

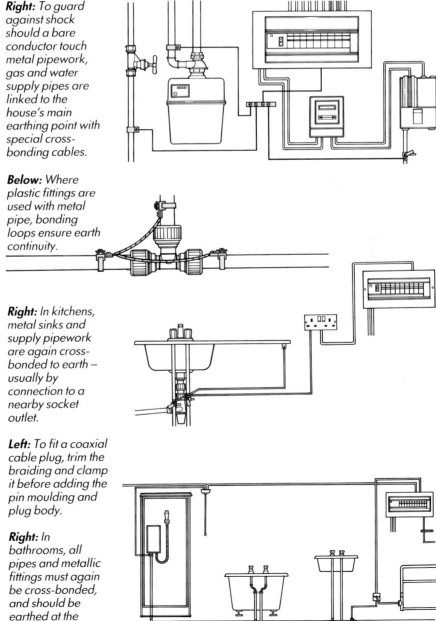

Right: To guard against shock should a bare conductor touch metal pipework, gas and water supply pipes are linked to the house's main earthing point with special cross-bonding cables.

Below: Where plastic fittings are used with metal pipe, bonding loops ensure earth continuity.

Right: In kitchens, metal sinks and supply pipework are again cross-bonded to earth – usually by connection to a nearby socket outlet.

Left: To fit a coaxial cable plug, trim the braiding and clamp it before adding the pin moulding and plug body.

Right: In bathrooms, all pipes and metallic fittings must again be cross-bonded, and should be earthed at the consumer unit.

SIMPLE REPAIR JOBS

Even if you never carry out any maintenance or alteration work on your home's wiring, you are likely to be faced with putting right any faults that may occur – either on the circuits themselves, or on the various lights and appliances that are connected to them. Often the fault is very simple to track down and rectify – a loose connection somewhere, or obvious physical damage such as that caused by drilling through an electric cable. Sometimes, however, the fault can be transient and rather more difficult to locate . . . and will be all the more dangerous for that.

In this section you will find advice on tracing electrical faults on the various parts of your wiring system, plus instructions on how to carry out a selection of simple repair jobs on common electrical appliances. If you are unsure of your ability to carry out these instructions safely, do not take a chance: call in a professional electrician instead.

TRACING ELECTRICAL FAULTS

When an electrical appliance will not work or all the lights go out, don't panic: there is usually a logical explanation and an equally obvious remedy. You need to work methodically through the checklist below, mentally ticking off possible causes as you eliminate them from your inquiries until you find what is causing the trouble.

1 Appliance fault

When an electrical appliance stops working, always unplug or isolate it from the mains before you do anything, especially if the fault involved a bang from inside the plug or any visible problem with the appliance.

If there is no immediately obvious fault, try plugging the appliance into another socket on a different circuit in the house – upstairs, say, if you were using it downstairs. If it works, the fault is at the original socket or on its circuit – see 3 right. If it does not work but another appliance does at the same socket, the fault is with the appliance.

Next, open the appliance plug and check that all the flex cores are properly connected to their terminals. Tighten or remake connections as necessary. If the appliance still does not work, replace the fuse with a new one of the correct rating.

Unplug the appliance again, and open it up so you can check the flex connections inside it. Remake them if necessary.

Next, check the continuity of the flex cores using a continuity tester, and fit a replacement flex if a fault shows up in any core.

If all these checks fail to find the fault, return the appliance to the appropriate service engineer for testing and repair.

2 Pendant light fault

When a pendant light stops working, first check that other lights on the same circuit are still working. If they are, switch off the affected light and replace the bulb. If they are not, suspect a circuit fault – see 3 below.

If replacing the bulb does not rectify the fault, switch off the power to the circuit at the consumer unit and open up the ceiling rose and lampholder so you can check for loose connections. Remake them if necessary.

Next, use a continuity tester to check the flex continuity between lampholder and rose, and replace the flex if a fault is found.

3 Circuit fault

If a whole lighting or power circuit fails, switch off all the lights or disconnect all the appliances on the circuit. Then turn off the power at the main switch on the consumer unit, and replace the appropriate circuit fuse or reset the miniature circuit breaker if it has tripped off. Restore the power and go round the affected circuit, turning on lights or plugging in appliances. Note which if any blow the circuit fuse or trip the MCB, and isolate it for repairs. Then switch off the mains, replace the fuse or reset the MCB again and restore the power once more.

If the circuit is still dead after you have replaced the fuse/reset the MCB, turn off the power again and check the circuit continuity by opening up faceplates, junction boxes and so on. Remake any faulty connections.

Where the cause of the circuit fault is obvious – you drilled through a cable, for example – turn off the power, expose the damaged

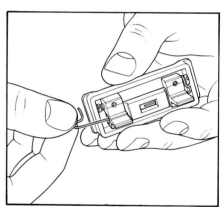

1. If a rewirable fuse blows, turn off the power and pull out the fuseholder. Unscrew the terminals. Remove burnt wire.

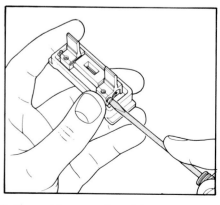

2. Thread in new wire of the correct rating and fix it to the terminals. NEVER use any other metallic object as a fuse.

cable and remake the connections inside a junction box.

If your system incorporates MCBs and you cannot reset any that have tripped off, this indicates that the fault is still present. Call an electrician if you are unable to locate it.

4 *System fault*

If the whole house is without power, check with neighbours to see if there is a power cut. Remember that a single-phase supply fault may affect only one house in three, so your immediate neighbour may still have power if his supply comes from another phase, while the house opposite yours may not if it is connected to the same phase as you are.

Next, check your own consumer unit if you have a residual current device protecting it, and attempt to reset it if it has tripped off. If you

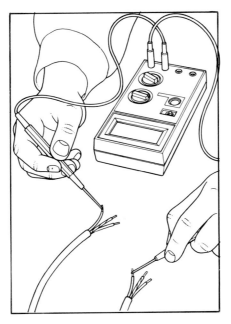

Above: *Use a test meter to check whether flex cores are damaged, by touching the probes to each core in turn.*

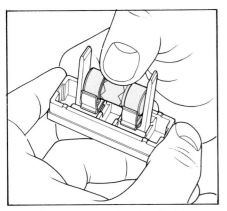

3. With some cartridge fuseholders, the fuse is a simple push-fit. Fuses of different ratings are different sizes.

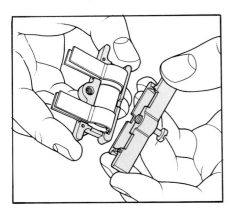

4. Sometimes, the fuse is held between wrap-around terminals, so you must dismantle the fuseholder to fit the fuse.

cannot reset it, the fault that tripped it is still present, and you should call an electrician.

If you appear to have a supply fault, call your local electricity authority's 24-hour emergency number (listed under Electricity in telephone directories). They will tell you when power will be restored if there is a power cut, or will send an engineer to check your supply and main system fuse.

REPLACING FUSES

When a circuit fuse blows, you must either replace the wire in the fuseholder or fit a new cartridge fuse, depending on which sort of fuseholder your system uses. With rewirable fuses you *must* use wire of the correct rating, so make sure you always have a supply to hand. *Never* repair a fuse with any other metallic object; if you do, the circuit will lose its vital fuse protection and someone could be electrocuted if a fault developed.

It is a good idea to keep a spare correctly-wired fuseholder for each fuseway so you can restore the power first and mend the fuse later.

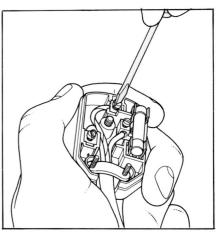

Above: *Check all connections within plugs.*
Below: *Test cartridge fuses across the open end of a switched-on metal torch.*

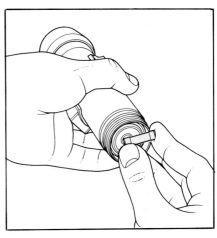

With cartridge fuses, which are of different sizes, you can fit only the correct replacement to a particular fuseholder. Again, keep spares near the consumer unit. *Never* try to repair a cartridge fuse.

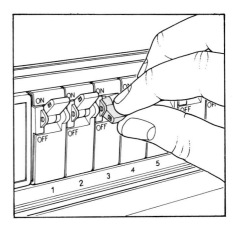

Above: *With MCBs, you cannot reset the switch until the circuit fault has been fixed.*

REPLACING FLEX

Flex is one of the most vulnerable components of your whole electrical system. On portable appliances it gets tugged this way and that and is regularly coiled up and uncoiled, while on other appliances it may be trodden on or tripped over at regular intervals. Even the flex on pendant lights can stretch and chafe as lampshades sway in the breeze. Eventually either the core conductors break or the insulation is split to reveal dangerous live cores. It is wise to inspect all flexes regularly.

It is acceptable to make a temporary repair to damaged flex using PVC insulating tape, but this should not be relied on to make a permanent repair. As soon as possible you should either cut out the damaged section and reconnect the cut ends with a one-part flex connector (see page 28), or else discard the old flex completely and fit a new length.

When you are working on an appliance flex, always unplug the appliance from the mains first. With flex to pendant lights, it is not enough to turn off the light at its switch. There will still be live connections within the ceiling rose, so you must turn off the power to the circuit at the consumer unit.

Always replace flex with the same type as was originally fitted, and make sure you use flex of the right current rating. The wattages each size can supply are: 0.5mm^2 – 720W; 0.75mm^2 – 1440W; 1.0mm^2 – 2400W; 1.5mm^2 – 3600W.

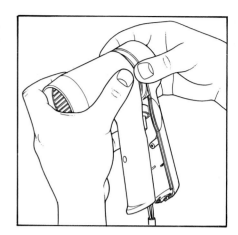

Above: To replace the flex on an appliance, unplug it and open the casing.

Below: Disconnect the flex cores from their terminals and free the flex from the cord grip.

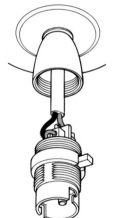

Left: To replace the flex in a pendant light, first turn off the power at the mains. Then open the rose and lampholder so you can disconnect the old flex and replace it with a new length.

Right: To replace the flex on a table lamp, unplug it from the mains. Then unscrew the lamp socket, disconnect the old flex cores and link them to the end of the new flex so you can draw it through the lamp body using the old flex as a pull-through. Prepare the cores on the new flex, and reconnect them to the lamp socket. On lamps with metallic parts, use three-core flex and connect the earth core to the terminal on the lampholder.

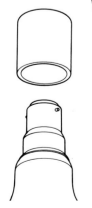

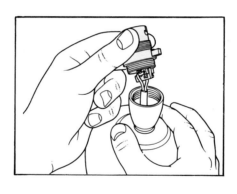

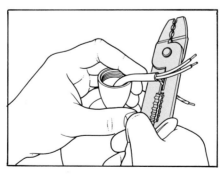

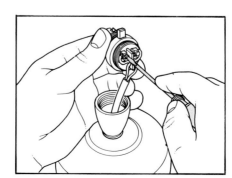

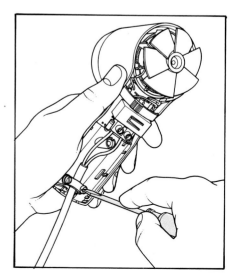

Below: Feed the new flex in through the grip, connect the cores to the terminals and tighten the cord grip on the flex sheath.

REPLACING DAMAGED CABLE

During the course of other do-it-yourself activities you may be unlucky enough to damage a hidden circuit cable – for example, when drilling holes in floorboards or walls. Assuming that the drill you are using is double-insulated, you will get little more than a nasty fright, but the damage to the cable will probably also cause a short circuit which will blow the circuit fuse.

Ensure that the power to the circuit concerned stays off by turning it off at the mains, so you can carry out a repair in safety. For cables below floorboards, the best way of making a repair is to cut through the cable cleanly, strip back the sheathing and core insulation and reconnect the cut ends at a three-terminal junction box, mounted on the side of a joist. Where the cable is buried in plaster, you must again

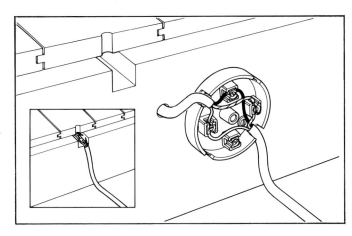

Right: If you damage a cable under a floor by drilling or nailing through it, cut out the damaged part and rejoin the cable ends as shown inside a junction box mounted on the side of a nearby joist.

link the cut ends of cable within an enclosure of some sort. The best way is to chisel out a recess in the wall surface at the point of damage to take a metal architrave box. You can then reconnect the cables using connector blocks to link like cores, and fit a blanking-off plate over the box. If this is recessed well into the wall, you can then fill over it.

If you drill through cable that is run in conduit, it is easier to replace the complete cable run since you can disconnect the cable from the wiring accessories it connects and draw it out. Use the old cable as a pull-through to draw the new length of cable into place. All you then have to do is reconnect its ends to the wiring accessories, and make good the hole.

REPLACING FITTINGS

It is easy to damage plugs or the faceplates of wiring accessories through carelessness, and if this occurs there is always a danger that someone could touch live wires or terminals, especially if a part of the plug or faceplate is actually missing.

If you find damage of this kind, carry out an emergency repair (see below) to minimize the danger, and replace the damaged component at the earliest opportunity.

EMERGENCY REPAIRS

If you crack a plug – by dropping it, for example – or damage the faceplate of a wiring accessory, take immediate steps to make it safe so there is no risk of anyone touching live parts. The best way of doing this is to use PVC insulating tape.

To repair a cracked plug, wrap the tape securely round the plug body. Where an accessory faceplate is cracked or broken, use strips of tape to repair the damage. Under no circumstances allow such repairs to become permanent.

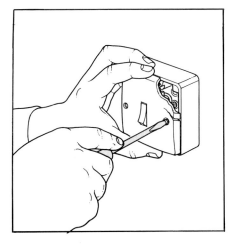

1. Unscrew the damaged faceplate.

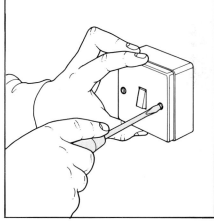

2. Fit a matching replacement.

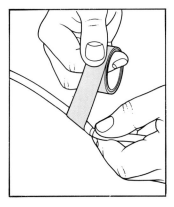

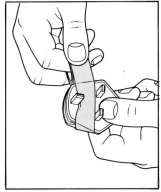

Left: Make a temporary repair to damaged flex by winding PVC insulating tape round it. Fit new flex to make a permanent repair. Make a cracked casing safe with insulating tape passed round it and between the pins.

REPAIRING PULL CORDS

Pull cords on ceiling switches are subjected to a lot of wear, and may eventually break. If the break occurs below the plastic connector, you can simply unscrew it and fit a new cord, which is sold complete with connector and pull toggle.

If the break occurs at the top, between the connector and the switch itself, you have to dismantle the switch to replace the short section of cord. Turn off the power, unscrew the switch faceplate and disconnect the cables. Then unscrew the switch mechanism from the faceplate, holding it so the spring inside does not fire bits everywhere, and carefully lift off the mechanism to reveal the knotted end of the pull

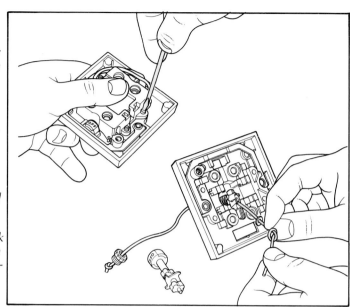

Right: To dismantle a cord-operated switch, turn off the power and unscrew the switch faceplate so you can disconnect the cable cores. Then hold the switch assembly while you undo the screws securing it to the faceplate, and lift it off so you can release the old cord and fit the new piece. Reassemble the switch and check that its on/off action works before reconnecting the supply cables and replacing the switch.

cord. Release the old cord, thread in a new piece and reassemble the switch. Finally link the other end to the connector.

REPLACING BRUSHES

Many domestic appliances incorporate an electric motor and the brush motor is the commonest type – it is found in washing machines, vacuum cleaners, food mixers, hairdriers and many power tools. The brushes are actually small carbon sticks which need replacing occasionally. On some appliances, the brush tubes are accessible from outside the appliance casing via screw-headed caps. In this case you simply undo

the cap, withdraw the old brush and spring and fit a replacement. Alternatively, you will have to dismantle the appliance to reach the motor.

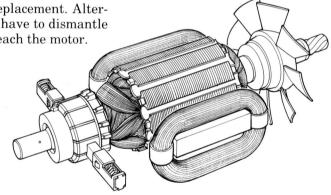

Right: The carbon brushes are held against the motor's commutator by springs. You may have to dismantle the appliance casing to gain access to them.

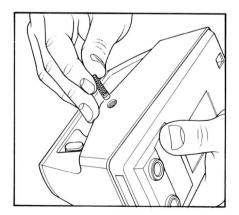

Above: Unplug the appliance, then examine the casing to locate the screws holding it on. Remove them and set aside.

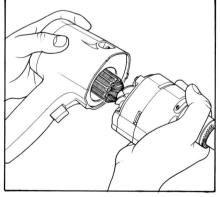

Above: Ease the motor gently out of the casing, taking care not to impose any strain on internal flex connections.

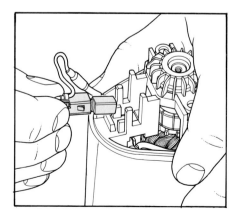

Above: Release the small clasps holding the brushes in place, clip new brushes to the springs and slot them into their tubes.

REPLACING HEATER AND KETTLE ELEMENTS

Many appliances contain a heating element. It may be exposed, as in an electric radiant fire; or enclosed, as in a kettle, a washing machine or a cooker hotplate. Whether you can replace a burnt-out element yourself depends on how accessible it is and whether you can obtain the correct spare part easily. The repairs dealt with here are generally simple to carry out, but if you have any doubts about your ability to carry out the job, leave it to a repair engineer.

Heater elements

It is usually a simple matter to replace the heating element in most wall-mounted radiant fires, since the fireclay type of element is generally secured to its terminals at each end by threaded nuts and silica elements fit into sockets. Make sure the appliance is unplugged first, then remove the safety guard so you can gain access to the terminal nuts. Undo these to release the old element; you may need pliers if the nuts are stiff or corroded. On some fires, you may have to remove terminal covers first.

Kettle elements

Many older electric kettles do not have an integral cut-out switch, so must be switched on and off at the socket into which they are plugged. Fitting a new element to this type of kettle is quite straightforward. You simply unscrew the shroud on the outside of the kettle, remove the fibre washer and lift the old element out. Clean any scale from around the opening, then fit the new element with the rubber washer on the inside and the fibre one on the outside. Tighten the shroud fully.

With an automatic kettle, you have to release the switch assembly to gain access to the nuts holding the element. You can then usually lift out the old element and fit the new one, but check the maker's instructions first.

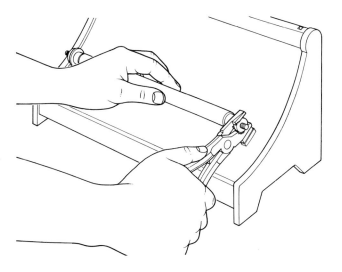

Left: To remove the element from a radiant fire, first unplug it. Then remove the guard, and any covers over the terminals, so you can unscrew the nuts securing the ends of the element to its terminals. Remove the old element and take it with you for identification when you buy the new one. Reverse the removal sequence to fit it.

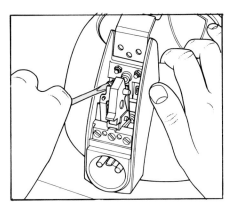 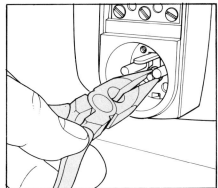

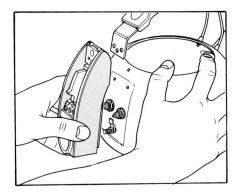

Above left: On an automatic kettle, remove the back cover plate so you can reach the screws holding the switch assembly.

Above: Use long-nosed pliers to free the nut securing the earth pin.

Left: Lift the switch assembly off.

Below: Unscrew the nuts holding the element in place, lift it out and reverse the procedure to fit the new one.

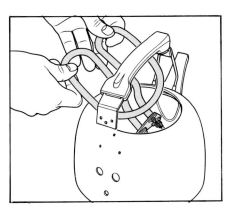 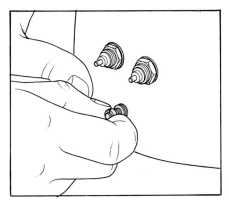

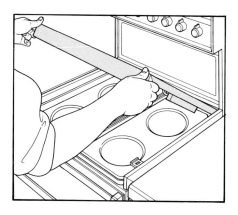

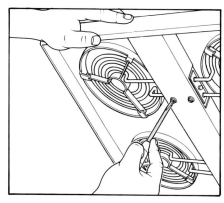

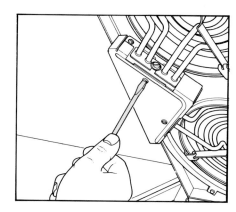

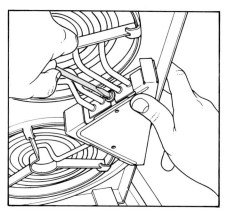

Above left: *Lift up the hob cover after releasing any screws holding it in place.*

Above and above right: *Release the screws holding the terminal cover plate, which may be central or to one side of the cooker.*

Left: *Disconnect the burnt-out element from its mounting and lift it out.*

Right: *Fit the new element, making sure it sits squarely on its supports.*

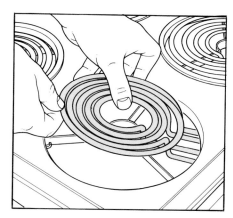

COOKER RINGS

If your cooker has ring or solid metal elements, it is usually possible to fit a replacement without having to call a service engineer. However, you should not attempt to replace oven or grill elements, or those on cera-mic or modern inset hobs.

Start by isolating the cooker from the mains, then lift the top hob plate to gain access to the element terminals. The hob plate may be secured by screws, or may lift up like a car bonnet. You can then remove the cover plate over the element termin-als, and see how the element itself is secured. Some plug in; others need unscrewing. Release the old element and take it with you when buying a replacement, so you can be sure of getting the correct part. Fit this by reversing the removal sequence and restore the power.

IRON ELEMENTS

With dry irons, the heating element is usually sandwiched between the iron soleplate and a layer of heat-resistant insulation. To gain access to it you have to remove the handle and cover assembly, then disconnect the element contact strips and temperature control spindle before releasing the pressure plate. On a steam iron, you generally have to replace the entire soleplate. Release the screws underneath it so you can lift the handle and water tank and remove the thermostat from its housing. Then unscrew the pressure plate, lift off the gasket and remove the soleplate.

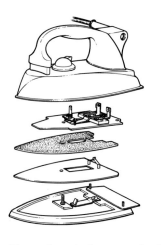

Above: *Dismantle a dry iron completely to replace the heating element, which is sandwiched between the soleplate and a layer of heat-resistant insulation.*

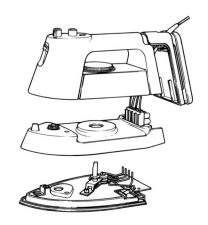

Above: *The element on a steam iron is not separate, like that on a dry iron; to replace it you usually have to renew the entire soleplate and element assembly.*

ELECTRICAL PROJECTS

WORK ON EXISTING CIRCUITS

This chapter is the first of four dealing with a wide range of individual electrical wiring projects, and covers work on existing circuits: such as adding extra light fittings or providing power for fixed appliances, which involve 'tapping into' an existing lighting or power circuit with the minimum of new wiring work. It also deals with ancillary wiring jobs such as central heating controls, TV aerial and telephone sockets, doorbells and burglar alarms.

For each job, you will find a clear circuit diagram showing the routes of new cables and explaining where everything fits, plus detailed wiring diagrams to help you connect up the various accessories and fittings correctly. The important part is always making the connection to the existing circuit, and all your options are spelt out.

EXTENDING LIGHTING CIRCUITS WITH JUNCTION BOXES

If you want to supply additional light fittings, one way of connecting into an existing lighting circuit is to cut into the circuit cable at a convenient point and connect the ends of the cut circuit cable into a 5-amp junction box.

You can do this in two ways. The first is to use a three-terminal box to connect in the spur cable. You then run the cable to wherever it is needed and provide the required switching connections at that point. The second method is to use a four-terminal box for the connection to the existing circuit cable, and connect in the switch cable for the new light at this junction box. The method you choose depends on which one is the more convenient to wire up and the more economical in terms of the amount of cable used.

There are two important points to remember when you are planning to extend a lighting circuit. The first is that you must connect into the circuit itself, not into switch cables or into cables running from four-terminal junction boxes to individual light fittings. You must therefore do some detective work to identify the correct cables.

The second point is that you cannot extend a lighting circuit indefinitely. Each circuit on a modern system is protected by a 5-amp circuit fuse, so can supply a maximum wattage of 1200W. Each lighting

Right: You can add extra lights to an existing lighting circuit by cutting four-terminal junction boxes into the main circuit cable, and running new cables on to serve the extra light and switch. You can do this on both junction-box and loop-in circuits.

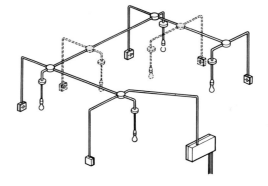

point is deemed in theory to consume 100W, irrespective of the actual size of bulb fitted, so the maximum number of lighting points permitted on each circuit is 12. In practice the number is generally limited to eight, so it is important to check how many lights each circuit already supplies before you extend it. If your circuits are fully 'booked' you have no option but to provide power for the new light from another circuit with spare capacity.

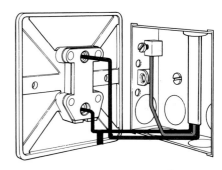

Above: At the new one-way switch, connect the cable cores to the switch and box.

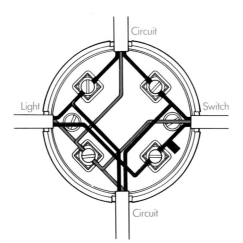

Above: Connect the cables to the new switch and light at a four-terminal junction box wired up as shown.

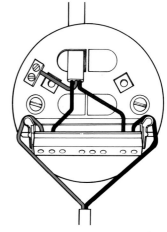

Above: Complete the new wiring by connecting the light cable and flex at the new rose.

EXTENDING LIGHTING CIRCUITS VIA LOOP-IN ROSES

If your lighting circuits are wired up on the loop-in principle – that is, the switch for each light is wired directly into the rose instead of to a separate junction box – you can extend the system by connecting a spur cable directly into the loop-in rose. Modern roses will accommodate up to four cables, so even an intermediate rose with three cables already can accept a fourth.

The spur cable cores are connected to the centre live, neutral and earth terminals of the rose, and the cable is then run to where it is needed. At that point the switching for the new light is also connected in – either at the new rose if one is being used, or via connector blocks within a conduit box if a light fitting is being used instead of a lampholder.

You can of course also extend your loop-in system by cutting in a new loop-in rose at a convenient point, as shown in the diagram below. Always make sure you cut into the main circuit cable, and not into a switch cable.

Right: You can insert loop-in roses into the circuit in the same way as for junction boxes (page 45). You can also connect spur cables into existing roses to feed new lights.

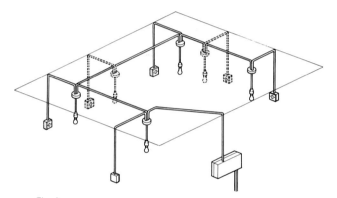

Left: The new rose has incoming and outgoing circuit cables, plus a new switch cable.

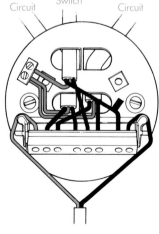

Above: If an extra light will be controlled by an existing switch, run a spur to it from the existing light and connect it as shown.

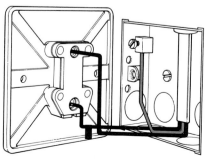

Left: Wire the one-way switch like this to control the new intermediate rose.

INSTALLING NEW LIGHT FITTINGS

The light fittings in many homes are nothing more adventurous than pendant lampholders hidden inside an array of decorative lampshades. However, with such a wide range of decorative light fittings now available, you can easily replace your roses and lampholders with something rather more attractive.

Some types of light fitting – flush-fitting lights in particular – have a terminal block on their baseplates designed for direct connection to the lighting circuit cable. Others generally have a short length of flex attached, and you have to connect this to the circuit cable.

Your first step in either case is to turn off the power supply to the circuit you are working on. If you are fitting a light where none exists, run in the new supply as described above and bring the spur cable to the point where the new light will be mounted. If, on the other hand, you are replacing an existing rose, unscrew its cover and note how many cables are present. One cable means the light is wired from a four-terminal junction box, while two or more indicate that loop-in wiring has been used. In the latter case, label the switch cable before disconnecting the cores from the rose baseplate, so you can reconnect them correctly to your new light.

Now remove the old rose. If there is just a single cable and you are mounting a fitting with an integral terminal block, connect the cable cores to the terminals (they will be marked L for live, N for neutral and E for earth) and screw the fitting to the ceiling.

Fitting a conduit box

For all other wiring arrangements you need to make the cable connections within a conduit box recessed into the ceiling. This is then concealed by the light fitting's baseplate – some fittings are designed with screw holes at 51mm (2in) centres, allowing them to be screwed direct to the threaded lugs at each side of the conduit box using M4 machine screws.

To mount the box, you need access to the void above the ceiling. The box should be screwed to a batten fixed between adjacent joists so that the lip of the box is flush with the

Right: Assemble a new pendant lampholder in this sequence, passing the flex through the lampholder cover before connecting its live and neutral cores to the lampholder terminals.

Left: With light fittings having a built-in terminal block, run cable to it from a four-terminal junction box, wired up as shown, and connect the cable cores directly to the fitting's terminals.

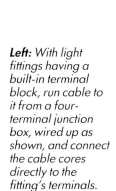

ceiling surface. This batten also provides a firm support for the light fitting itself if it is not being mounted on the conduit box. Place the batten over the desired light position, then cut a hole in the ceiling with a padsaw, secure the batten and screw the box to it. Feed in the supply cable and connect it to the flex on the light fitting – red (live) to brown, black (neutral) to blue and earth to earth – using connector blocks.

If you are replacing an existing loop-in rose, you need four connector

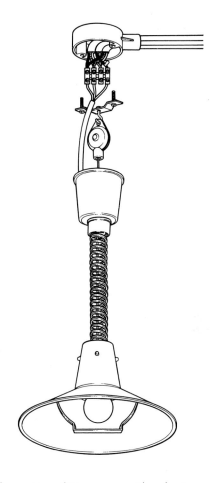

Above: Many fittings come with a short length of flex, and you must connect these to the circuit wiring using connector blocks housed within a recessed conduit box.

blocks rather than three to allow for the switch cable. Link the cable cores to the flex as shown below.

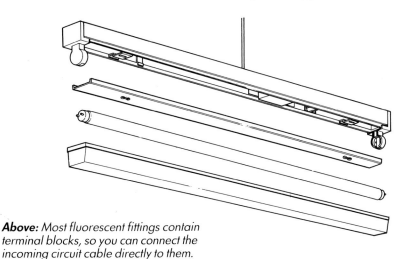

Above: Most fluorescent fittings contain terminal blocks, so you can connect the incoming circuit cable directly to them.

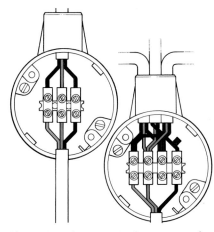

Above: Use three terminal connectors for loop-in wiring connections, and four with junction-box wiring, wired up as shown here.

INSTALLING WALL LIGHTS

The only significant difference between wall lights and ceiling-mounted fittings is their position; the principles of providing them with a power supply and switch control are the same. The obvious drawback with installing wall lights is the need to disturb existing decorations, unless you are prepared to put up with surface-mounted wiring until you redecorate, when you can recess the cable into the plaster.

The first step is to decide on the position of the fittings, where you want switches to control them, and at what point you are going to pick up their power supply from existing circuits. The simplest situation is where wall lights will replace the existing central pendant light and you intend to use the existing switch to turn them on and off. Here all you have to do is replace the rose with a junction box above the ceiling, and run cable from there to each light. It is more complicated if you want to retain the existing centre light and have switching of several wall lights from two or more positions (see page 52 for more details).

Remember that you can supply power for your wall lights from either a lighting circuit as described on pages 45-46, or from a power circuit. Use whichever method is more convenient in your case. The power circuit option involves taking a spur from a socket outlet or a 30-amp junction box, running the spur cable to a switched fused connection unit fitted with a 5-amp fuse, and then running further cable to the light fitting itself. Such a spur can supply up to five lights. You can either use the FCU to provide on/off control, or have independent switching via a four-terminal junction box.

You can now plan the cable routes in detail and start work on actually installing the lights. Each should be mounted over an enclosure recessed into the wall surface. Use a standard conduit box if the fitting has fixing

Right: So long as your existing lighting circuit has enough spare capacity, you can cut in a four-terminal junction box at a convenient point and run cable in series to your new wall lights. With this the lights are controlled by a single one-way switch.

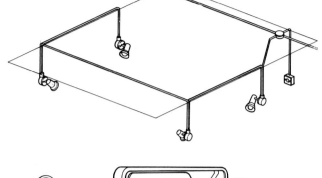

Right: Or, take a spur from a nearby power circuit, running it first to an FCU containing a 5-amp fuse. From here the cable can run on to one or more lights. The FCU can act as the light switch, or you can fit a junction box between FCU and light to provide independent switching.

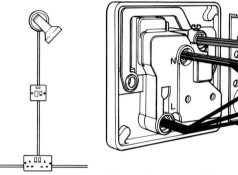

Above: The spur cable cores go to the FEED terminals, the light cable cores to LOAD.

holes at 51mm (2 in) centres or has a large baseplate which will cover the box completely and allow fixings to be made into the wall itself. Alternatively, use a flush-mounted metal architrave box instead.

Next, cut a chase for the cable to run into the enclosure, and run in the cable. Connect it to the light fitting using connector blocks as for flush-mounted ceiling lights, and mount the fitting.

What happens to the other end of the cables to each light depends on the wiring method you have selected. One of the most common arrangements is for the cables feeding the lights to be connected together at a three-terminal junction box, with like cores linked to like. From here a single cable is run to a four-terminal box which is cut into the main lighting circuit cable, and where the switch cable controlling the lights is also connected in.

Luminaire support couplers
Some modern light fittings are supplied wired to a special plug which is designed to be inserted in a matching wall socket. This takes the place

of the recessed conduit or architrave box in the wall. The advantage of this is that the light fitting can be removed easily during decorating, and can be easily exchanged for another in the future.

Above: Luminaire support couplers are two-part plug-and-socket connectors that allow you to take down the light by unplugging it.

TRACK LIGHTING

Track lighting consists of a length of special track which is fixed to the ceiling and connected to a power supply just like an ordinary light fitting. You can then mount individual light fittings on the track wherever you choose – a useful arrangement when, for example, you want to spotlight individual features in the room.

The track is generally sold in lengths of 1.2, 2.4 and 3.6m (approximately 4 ft, 7 ft 10 in and 11 ft 8 in), and you can join lengths together with special electrical/mechanical connectors to give you the exact arrangement you require. It can even turn corners or run into T-joints. The track conceals the electrical conductors that run along its length, and it is impossible to touch live parts when connecting or disconnecting the lights using their special plugs. The track is either fixed in place using brackets screwed to the ceiling joists, or may

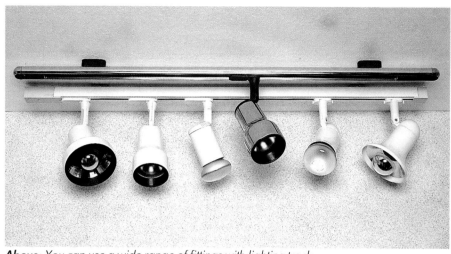

Above: You can use a wide range of fittings with lighting track.

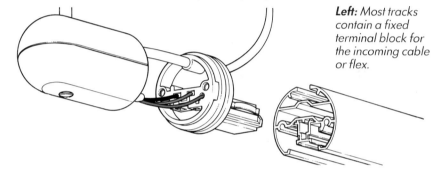

Left: Most tracks contain a fixed terminal block for the incoming cable or flex.

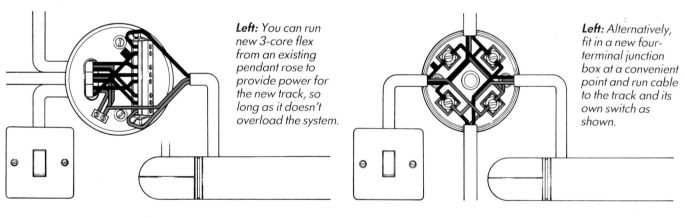

Left: You can run new 3-core flex from an existing pendant rose to provide power for the new track, so long as it doesn't overload the system.

Left: Alternatively, fit in a new four-terminal junction box at a convenient point and run cable to the track and its own switch as shown.

be suspended from the ceiling.

The electrical connections are similar to those for a fluorescent light, with the supply cable entering the top of the track and being connected to the track terminal block which is usually at one end. The power supply can be brought in via a spur from a loop-in rose or a junction box, as with any other light fitting. Alternatively, you can connect a new length of 3-core flex from a nearby unused ceiling rose. However, such arrangements should be

used only if the track and other lights on the same circuit do not consume more than 5 amps. Most tracks are rated at 16 amps, so if you want to use the system to its full capacity you will have to wire it up on its own separate circuit (see pages 74-75).

Fittings for track lighting systems

All track systems offer a choice of several different light fittings, but

these are not interchangeable between brands, so once you have chosen your track you must use fittings from that manufacturer. Spotlights of various types are the most widely available, but you can also have eyeball, globe, flood and parabolic reflector lamps. Some ranges even include pendant lamps in a variety of period designs.

You can buy low-voltage fittings which have their own transformers so you can reduce running costs on multi-lamp installations.

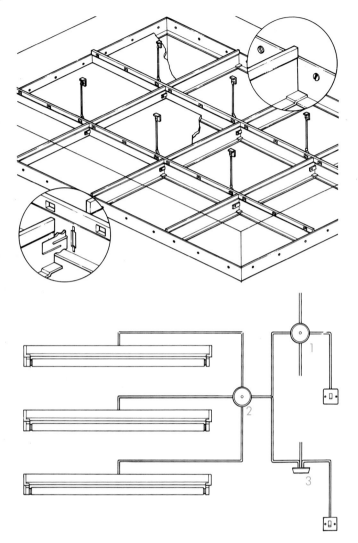

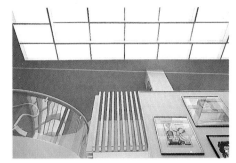

Left: *Suspended ceilings come in kit form. Perimeter mouldings support main cross bearers, and intermediate bearers slot between these to form the grid into which the ceiling panels fit.*

Right: *Most systems offer translucent panels in a range of patterns and colours, and you can also specify solid panels if you want to give your ceiling a 'dark' perimeter.*

Left: *The ceiling is lit by a number of fluorescent tubes, wired up in parallel to a three-terminal junction box (see detail 2). The power can be supplied from either a four-terminal junction box (detail 1) or from a redundant loop-in ceiling rose (detail 3).*

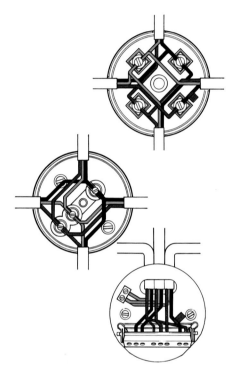

ILLUMINATED CEILINGS

Illuminated ceilings are just what their name implies: a translucent suspended ceiling lit from above, usually with fluorescent tubes, to give the effect of a uniform diffused light. The latest fire regulations prohibit the use of the cheaper translucent panels, so if you decide to fit a suspended ceiling of this type, make sure that the ceiling panels you use are fire-resistant.

There are several systems on the market all broadly similar in principle and consisting of a lightweight aluminium grid that carries square or rectangular panels. The first step in installing the ceiling is to fix edge trims to the walls all round the room at the level chosen for the new ceiling. You can position it at any level which gives adequate head-room, so long as there is sufficient space between it and the ceiling for the light fittings to be installed.

You then bridge the room with long main cross beams, which rest on the edge trims and are spaced to match the size of the ceiling panels being used. In wide rooms, these beams may need extra support to prevent them sagging. This usually takes the form of wires hanging down from the ceiling joists, or rigid support brackets. Finally, shorter cross-pieces are fitted between the main beams to frame the individual panels, which simply rest in place on the beams and cross-pieces.

The lighting above a suspended ceiling of this sort is generally pro-vided by one or more fluorescent lights wired in tandem. The number of tubes required, and the total wattage needed for good illumination of the room, depends on the room size and your choice of ceiling panels; the system manufacturer will guide you on this point.

You can provide the lighting in one of two ways. The first method is to install the required number of separate fluorescent fittings, linking the supply cables to each light at a three-terminal junction box and then supplying that by a spur from a nearby lighting circuit. A less ex-pensive alternative is to fit separate tubes and starter/ballast units; fly leads link each control unit to its tube, and cable links the units to the junction box as shown above.

RECESSED LIGHTS

There is a wide range of light fittings available which are designed to be recessed into the ceiling surface instead of being mounted on it. These include downlighters, spotlights and rotating eyeball fittings, and they are often used in groups controlled from a single switch – in other words, several lights are wired in series from a single power supply connection.

As with all other additions to existing lighting circuits, your first step in planning to install one or more recessed lights is to decide on the light position(s) and work out the best point to make the connection to the existing circuit. Again, check that the lights you propose to install will not overload the circuit; if you exceed the recommended limit of eight lights per circuit, you will have to provide a new circuit to prevent overloading.

Whichever supply option you choose, the electrical connections are quite straightforward. Bring the incoming power supply cable to a four-terminal junction box, and connect in the switch cable here in the usual way. The next step depends on the relative positions of the lights themselves. You can either run a spur cable on to a three-terminal junction box sited close to the lights, and link each light to this junction box with its own feed cable, or you can simply loop the cable from one light to the next.

At the light fittings themselves, you will usually find a terminal block on the top of the fitting's framework or casing; simply connect the incoming circuit cable cores to the right terminals.

Recessed light fittings are designed to be a push fit in a circular hole cut in the ceiling, and are generally light enough not to need additional support. To install the fitting, check that the mounting position is clear of joists above and use the template supplied by the manufacturer to draw a hole on the ceiling. Use a padsaw to cut a neat

circle, then simply slot the light in place ready for connecting to the circuit wiring.

LOW-VOLTAGE LIGHTING

As an alternative to mains-voltage fittings, you can install special lights that run on low voltages via a

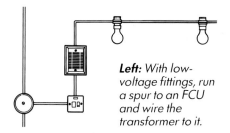

Above: Several types of recessed lights: downlighters, spotlights and rotating eyeballs.

Above: You can either link the lights via junction boxes, or wire them in series.
Left: Take the power supply to a four-terminal junction box where the switch and light cables are connected in.

Left: With low-voltage fittings, run a spur to an FCU and wire the transformer to it.

transformer which can be concealed in the void above the ceiling. These lights are smaller and neater than mains-voltage versions, and their halogen bulbs give a cool, white light that is perfect for highlighting features or providing decorative mood lighting effects in the room where they are installed.

Typical fittings include spotlights, eyeballs and wall lighters, and each consumes around 20 watts, so you can have a run of light fittings without overloading your existing lighting circuits. All you have to do is pick the correct transformer for the number of lights you plan to install, and provide a power supply to the transformer from a convenient connection point on the existing lighting circuit.

TWO-WAY SWITCHING

Most lights in the home are controlled by a single switch, usually sited near the room door; this is known as one-way switching. However, there are several situations where it is more convenient to control lights from more than one position. Examples include switching the landing light from upstairs or downstairs, or having bedside lights switched by the bed as well as by the bedroom door. Where two switch positions are provided, the system is known as two-way switching.

The principle of two-way switching is simple. The light to be controlled is linked to one of the switches in the usual way, and this switch is then linked to the second switch by strapping wires so that either switch will control the light. The switches used must be special two-way ones; these have three terminals which are usually marked C (for common), L1 and L2. (Some brands are marked L1, L2 and L3 or simply 1, 2 and 3.) The link between the two switches is made using special three-core-and-earth cable, which has cores colour-coded red, yellow and blue for identification (all are technically live).

The switch cable from the light is taken to the first switch, and its red and black cores are connected to the

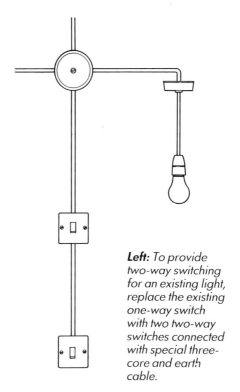

Left: To provide two-way switching for an existing light, replace the existing one-way switch with two two-way switches connected with special three-core and earth cable.

L1 and L2 terminals respectively. You should flag the black core with red PVC tape to show that it is live. The two switches are then linked with the three-core cable; the standard wiring convention is to link the two C terminals with the red core, and to link the L1 and L2 terminals on the two switches with the blue and yellow cores as shown.

Where you want to provide two-

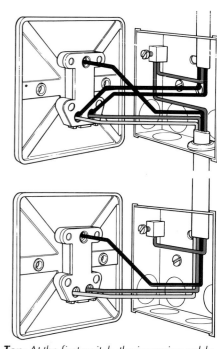

Top: At the first switch, the incoming cable is connected to the L1 and L2 terminals, and the outgoing one is linked to all three.

Above: At the second switch, the cores of the three-core and earth cable are connected to the same terminals as at the first switch.

way switching for more than one light – a pair of bedside wall lights, for example – you can save on unnecessary cable runs by using a multi-terminal junction box to provide power to the lights.

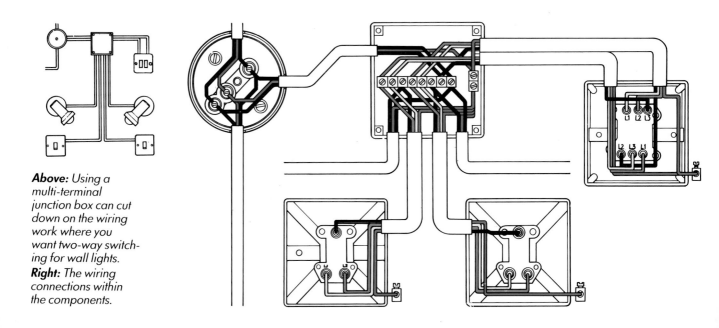

Above: Using a multi-terminal junction box can cut down on the wiring work where you want two-way switching for wall lights.
Right: The wiring connections within the components.

Stairwell switching

One situation where two-way switching is a must rather than a luxury is on the landing, the staircase and in the hall.

How you provide two-way switching of your staircase lighting depends on what switching arrangements exist already. Many homes already have partial two-way switching. The usual arrangement enables you to control the landing light from upstairs or downstairs, but the hall light from downstairs only. It is common to find that older homes contain no two-way switching at all.

If you have one-way switching only, you need to replace each existing one-way switch with a two-gang two-way switch. At the landing switch position, connect the cores of the existing landing light switch cable to the L1 and L2 terminals of the switch gang on the left (when viewed from the back of the switch). Then use three-core-and-earth cable to link this left-hand gang upstairs to the left-hand gang of the downstairs switch.

At the hall switch, connect the hall light switch cable cores to the L1 and L2 terminals of the right-hand gang, again as viewed from the back of the switch, and link this to the right-hand gang of the landing switch with three-core cable. With the wiring completed and the switches fitted to their mounting boxes, the left-hand switch at either position will control the hall light, and the right-hand switch will control the landing light.

If you already have partial two-way switching as described above, all you need to do is replace the one-gang two-way switch on the landing with a two-gang two-way switch. Reconnect the existing landing switch cable cores to one gang of the switch and use an extra run of three-core-and-earth cable to link the other gang to the existing two-gang two-way switch in the hall, altering the connections to the gang controlling the hall light to provide two-way switching.

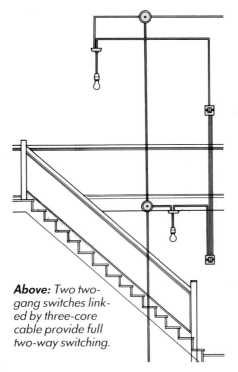

Above: Two two-gang switches linked by three-core cable provide full two-way switching.

Intermediate switching

You may want to control a particular light from more than two switch positions – for example, if you have a

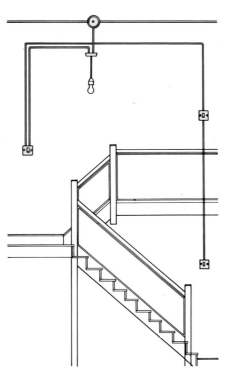

Above: Adding an intermediate switch between two two-way ones gives you switch control from three locations.

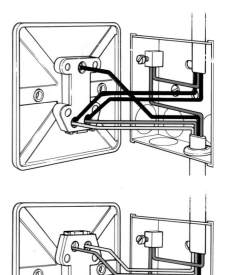
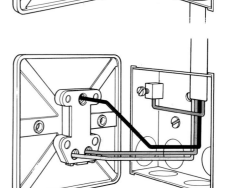

Above: Link the red cores with a connector block in the intermediate switch (centre).

long landing and want to operate the landing lights from outside each bedroom. To do this you need switches called intermediate switches, which have four terminals.

The switch cable from the light(s) to be controlled is connected to a two-way switch as for ordinary two-way switching. Three-core-and-earth cable is run from here to one or more intermediate switches, and on to a two-way switch at the most remote switch position; this last switch is wired up as usual. At each intermediate switch, the blue and yellow cores are connected to the switch terminals, and the red are linked by a connector block in the mounting box.

FITTING EXTERIOR LIGHTS

Good lighting outside your home is vital for several reasons. It helps you and your visitors to see the way safely to the front door at night, it means you can enjoy sitting or entertaining on the patio after dark, and above all it improves your home security – prowlers and would-be burglars hate the light. By installing light fittings at various points on the outside walls of your house, you can meet all these requirements.

The first step is to choose your light fittings according to the job they are to do. For example, you could fit decorative lights beside your front door, plain bulkhead lights to illuminate the side path, globe lights at the back to light up the patio, and some floodlights to shine on the driveway. Whichever type of fitting you choose, make sure it is labelled as being suitable for exterior use before you buy.

Next, decide on where the lights will be mounted so you can plan the cable routes accordingly. It is generally best to bring the supply cables through the house wall directly behind each fitting to minimize the risk of damage or water penetration. Then look at the connection facilities provided on the light itself. If there is a fixed terminal block, you can wire the supply cable directly into the fitting and simply mount it on the wall. If there is just a flex tail, you will need to recess a conduit box into the outside wall to contain the

Above: A selection of exterior light fittings now available. When buying, check that the fitting is suitable for outdoors.

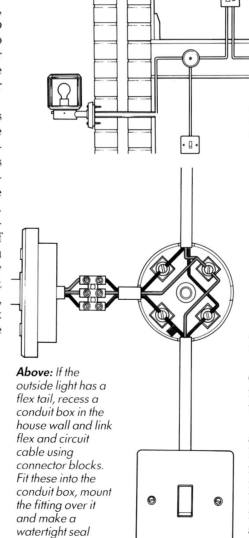

Left: A simple way of providing a power supply for an outside light is via a fused connection unit on a power circuit spur.

Above: If the outside light has a flex tail, recess a conduit box in the house wall and link flex and circuit cable using connector blocks. Fit these into the conduit box, mount the fitting over it and make a watertight seal between the two.

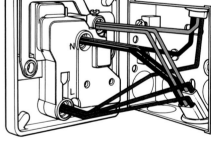

Above: Connect the spur cable supplying the fused connection unit at a ring socket.

connector blocks linking cable to flex, and then mount the light fitting's baseplate over it.

The actual electrical connections are identical to those for adding a light indoors. Simply pick a convenient point to connect into an existing circuit – light or power – and link up the required wiring accessories to provide power to the lights and a separate switching facility at a convenient location.

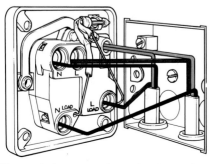

Above: At the connection unit, wire up the feed and load cables to their terminals.

Security lights

Any exterior lighting will help to deter prowlers from approaching your property, but even better protection is provided by exterior light fittings which are controlled by a passive infra-red (PIR) sensor. This detects the heat given off by a body (or even a car engine) entering its field of view, and immediately switches on the lights. A variable time switch turns them off again after a pre-set period of time, and a photocell deactivates the light during daylight hours.

You can install PIR-controlled lighting in two ways. The first is to buy a light fitting with its own integral sensor and to mount this on the outside wall so its field of view covers the main approach to the home. Some versions allow you to wire in additional ordinary lights to the sensor unit, so providing better light levels around the house exterior. The second method is to link a number of ordinary outside light fittings to a separate sensor (or sensors, if you want to guard front and back).

In either case, you can take the power supply for the light(s) either from an indoor light circuit (so long as the number of lights fitted will not overload the circuit), or from a power circuit via a fused connection unit fitted with a 5-amp fuse.

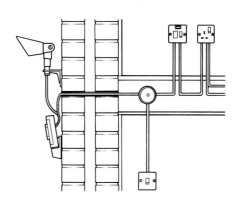

Above right: *Security lights may incorporate individual passive infra-red (PIR) sensors, or one sensor may serve several lights.*
Right: *Wire up outside security lights as for other exterior lighting, via a fused spur taken from a nearby power circuit. The four-terminal junction box provides separate switching.*

DIMMER SWITCHES

Dimmer switches allow you to vary the brightness of the lights they control, usually by turning a rotary control knob. On some cheaper types you turn the knob fully anti-clockwise to switch the light off. With others there may be a separate on/off switch, or else you push the rotary knob in to turn the light off and in again to turn it back on.

One-gang dimmers are the most common type, but two-gang versions are also available. All are suitable for two-way switching, and installing one in place of an existing switch simply involves disconnecting the existing switch cable and reconnecting it to the dimmer. However, there are several points to remember when choosing a dimmer switch. The first is that ordinary dimmers will not dim fluorescent lights; you need a special type of dimmer for this. The second is that dimmers operate properly only between a lower and upper wattage limit, so you must check that the one you intend to buy matches the wattage of the light(s) it is to control. Lastly, some dimmers need deeper-than-average mounting boxes.

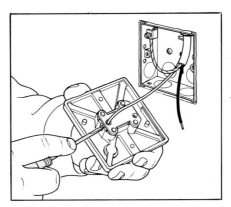

Above: *To fit a dimmer in place of a plate-switch, turn off the power and remove the faceplate so you can disconnect the cable.*

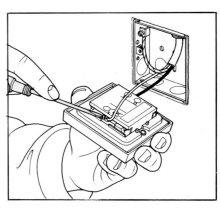

Above: *After checking that the dimmer will fit the existing mounting box, reconnect the cable cores to the dimmer terminals.*

Right: *Dimmers are available in one- and two-gang versions in a wide range of styles and finishes. The commonest have rotary knobs which you turn to alter the light level. Most also feature a push-on/push-off action, allowing you to switch the light off and on again, wherever you wish, without altering the pre-set light level.*

CONVERTING SOCKETS

Many homes do not have enough socket outlets to cope with the multitude of electrical appliances that we use today. This is at best a nuisance and at worst a danger; there is a temptation to run long flexes across rooms – a trip hazard – and to use adaptors at existing sockets, which can cause overloading of the wiring and damage to the socket itself.

Modern or recently rewired homes will generally have a double socket at each outlet position, but in older homes you are likely to find that many of the outlets are only single sockets. One way to increase the number of sockets you have is therefore to replace any single sockets in the home with double (or triple) ones. The advantage of this is that

no actual wiring work is involved – the power supply is simply disconnected from the old socket and re-connected to the new one, which is then fitted in its place.

There are two points to consider before you carry this out, however. Firstly, make sure that your wiring is in good condition and can carry the extra load. In older homes with radial power circuits that have not been rewired, you must not fit modern 13-amp sockets to cable that originally supplied 2-amp or 5-amp round-hole sockets. If your existing sockets are wired with rubber-sheathed cable, get a professional electrician to check its condition before you proceed. If the cable is already nearing the end of its life, any load could cause a fire.

Secondly, think about how you will actually carry out the change-over, following the instructions be-

low. If you have surface-mounted sockets and are happy to have the new ones surface-mounted too, basically you will simply remove the existing one-gang box from the wall and mount the new box in its place. If your existing sockets are flush-mounted, the easiest way of carrying out the conversion is to fit a plastic surface-mounted box over the existing flush box. Check first that there is enough cable in the box to allow easy connection of the cable cores to the new socket faceplate.

If you prefer to flush-mount your new sockets, you will have to chop recesses behind old surface-mounted sockets or remove existing one-gang flush boxes so you can widen the opening to accept the new, larger box. In this case, check first where the cable enters the box, so you do not chop through it while enlarging the hole if it enters from either side.

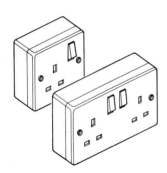

Option 1: *Convert an existing surface-mounted single socket to a surface-mounted double one – the easiest changeover.*

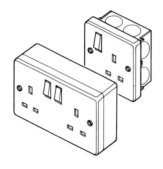

Option 2: *Fit a double surface-mounted socket over an existing flush box after removing the old single faceplate.*

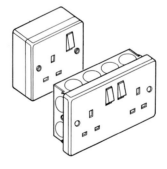

Option 3: *Remove the existing surface-mounted box and cut a recess for a new double flush mounting box.*

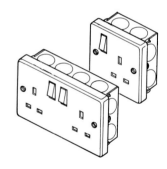

Option 4: *Remove an existing flush single mounting box and enlarge the recess to accept a new flush double box.*

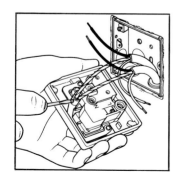

1. To convert a single flush socket to a surface-mounted double one, remove and disconnect the old faceplate.

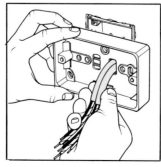

2. Remove a knockout in the back of the new box, and draw the circuit cables into the box through it.

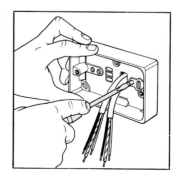

3. Position the new box over the old flush one, and use the old faceplate screws to fix it to the lugs.

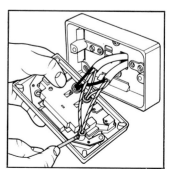

4. Complete the conversion by connecting the circuit cable cores to the new double faceplate.

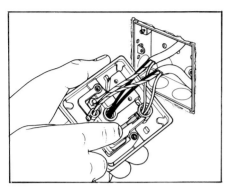

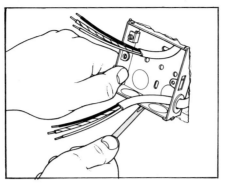

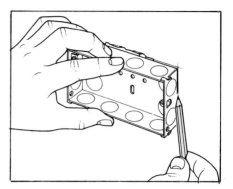

1. For a flush single to flush double conversion, start by unscrewing the old faceplate. Then disconnect the cables.

2. Undo the screws securing the box in the recess. Then cut round it with a knife to free it, and carefully ease it out.

3. Hold the new double box in position and mark its outline on the wall. Position it to avoid damaging the cables.

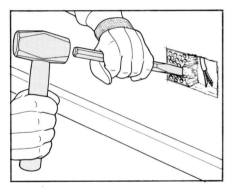

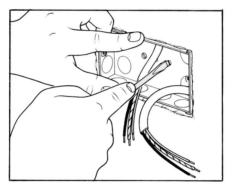

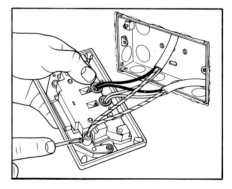

4. Honeycomb the masonry with drill holes. Then use a cold chisel and club hammer to enlarge the recess.

5. Remove a knockout from the flush box, fit grommets and feed in cables. Fit the box and secure it with screws.

6. Reconnect the cable cores to the terminals on the new faceplate, then secure the faceplate on its box.

Carrying out the conversion

Once you have decided how you intend to make the changeover, buy as many new sockets and mounting boxes as you need for the job. Check whether the earth cores within your existing sockets are covered with PVC sleeving; if they are bare, buy some green/yellow earth sleeving. Fit a length to each core as you reconnect the cables to your new sockets.

If your existing one-gang sockets are the 13-amp type, do not throw them away. Instead, buy special dual mounting boxes – flush or surface, as appropriate – which will accept two single socket faceplates side by side and will effectively give you a number of additional sockets at virtually no cost. You can also mount fused connection units next

to single sockets on these dual boxes if they suit your requirements.

Start work by turning off the power to the circuit you will be working on, and check that the circuit wiring is dead. Undo the screws holding the faceplate of the first socket to its mounting box and gently ease it away from the wall. If the walls are painted, you may find that the socket is 'glued' to the wall by paint along its edges; in this case, cut round the faceplate first with a sharp handyman's knife to free it and minimize the risk of damaging the decorations.

Now disconnect the cable cores from their terminals on the back of the single socket, and set this aside. The next step depends on whether the old socket was flush- or surface-mounted, and which option you have chosen for the new one.

For a surface-to-surface conversion, simply unscrew the old box, remove it and fit the new one in its place after removing a knockout for the cable(s). For a flush-to-surface conversion, position the new box over the existing one and secure it with screws and wallplugs. For a surface-to-flush conversion, remove the old box and chop a recess in the wall to accept the new mounting box. For a flush-to-flush conversion, remove the old box and enlarge the existing recess to take the new one.

With the box conversion complete, loosen the terminal screws on the new socket, and connect the cores to their correct terminals: live (red) to the terminal marked L, neutral (black) to N and earth to E. Fit a length of green/yellow PVC sleeving over the earth core first if it is not sleeved. Then attach the faceplate.

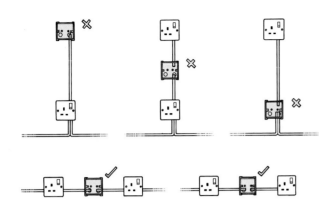

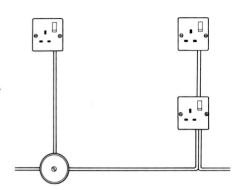

Left: *You cannot add spurs to sockets on or already supplying a spur (top), but you can use sockets on a ring or radial circuit.*

Right: *You can wire spurs into 30-amp junction boxes instead of wiring them from sockets on the circuit.*

INSTALLING EXTRA SOCKETS

You can add sockets to your existing power circuits in one of three ways: by connecting a spur cable to an existing socket outlet; by wiring the spur cable into the circuit using a 30-amp three-terminal junction box; or by cutting into the circuit cable and connecting the cut ends at the socket (you can do this only if there is enough slack on the cable beneath the floorboards for it to reach the proposed socket position). The method you choose will depend on where the new socket is to be sited.

As long as your existing circuits are modern ring or radial ones wired in PVC-sheathed cable, the only limit to the number of sockets you can add is that the number of sockets run as spurs must not exceed the number on the main circuit itself. The only restrictions are on the floor area each circuit can serve – 100sq m (1075 sq ft) for a ring main, 50sq m (540 sq ft) for a 30-amp radial circuit and 20sq m (215 sq ft) for a 20-amp radial – so if you are adding a socket in a room by a different circuit, check that the additional floor area of this room will not exceed the limit for the circuit to which you are connecting the extra socket.

If you have old radial circuits you may be able to add sockets to circuits protected by a 15-amp fuse, but ask a professional electrician to advise you on whether this will be safe.

To add an extra socket, you will need the socket itself, a flush- or surface-mounting box, enough cable to run the spur from the connection point to the new socket position, rubber grommets to protect the cable from chafing if you are using a flush box and lastly some green/yellow earth sleeving.

Wiring from a socket

Connecting your spur cable into an existing socket outlet is generally the easiest option, especially if the new socket is to be installed back-to-back with the existing one since the cable runs straight through the wall to the new socket position. Where the new socket is more remote, you will have to decide whether to surface-mount the cable or to lift floorboards and cut chases in the plaster to conceal it.

Remember that you cannot con-

Below: *A socket outlet on the main ring circuit has two cables. The cores should be twisted together in pairs as shown, or may be uncut and crimpled into a U-shape.*

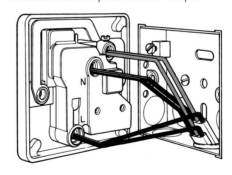

Below: *Connect spur cables to ring or radial circuits at convenient points using 30-amp three terminal junction boxes. Cable cores are linked like to like.*

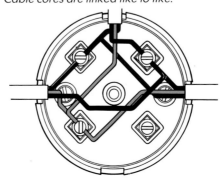

Below: *Run the spur cable into a main circuit socket outlet through a rubber grommet, and connect the cable cores to the terminals as shown. Sleeve the bare earth core.*

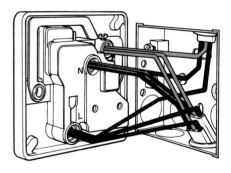

Below: *At the new spur socket, run the cable into the mounting box as before, and connect the cable cores to the live, neutral and earth terminals on the socket faceplate.*

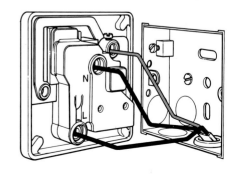

nect your spur cable to any socket; the wiring regulations allow spur cables to be connected only to sockets on the main circuit, and only one spur per socket is permitted. So you cannot add a spur to a socket that is itself wired as a spur, and you cannot wire a second spur cable into a socket that already supplies one.

You must therefore check the socket you propose to use to establish its status, and this can be quite difficult in some cases. You may find one, two or three cables present. A socket with three cables already supplies a spur, so can be ruled out. A socket with just one cable is probably on a spur, but it could be the last socket on a radial circuit. Check this by following the cable route back to the next socket.

A socket with two cables is the most difficult to check. It may be on a ring circuit, or it may be an intermediate socket on a radial circuit; either can be used to connect in your spur cable. However, it may be the intermediate socket on an old spur – former wiring regulations allowed spurs to supply two sockets instead of just the one now permitted – and this cannot be used to feed another spur. Again, following the circuit cable is the best way to identify your socket; you can also use a continuity tester (see above) to check whether such a socket is on a ring main.

Once you are satisfied that the

Right: You can check whether a socket with two cables present is on a ring circuit by using a continuity tester. Turn off the power, open up the socket and disconnect the faceplate. Link the two live cores with the probes of the tester. If the socket is on a ring, the tester will show a continuous circuit

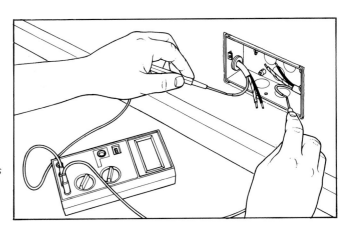

socket you propose to use for your spur cable connection is on the main circuit, you can start work on running in the spur. There is no need to turn off the power at this stage, until you are ready to make the final connection. Start by fitting the mounting box at the new socket position, if you are installing a flush box use a rubber grommet in the knockout to prevent the cable sheath chafing, and then run the spur cable back from there to the socket into which it will be connected, concealing or surface-mounting it as appropriate. Switch off the power to the circuit you will be working on, and check that it is dead.

Unscrew the socket faceplate and ease it away from the wall so you can see where the cable knockout is. There should be room for up to three cables through one knockout, but if there is not you will have to remove another from the box. Feed in the spur cable, and trim it back so you leave enough to make the connections without overfilling the box. Prepare the cable cores, connect them into the faceplate terminals and carefully fold the cables back into the box so you can attach the faceplate again. Restore the power and check that your spur is working.

Using a junction box

You may prefer to connect your spur directly to the circuit cable using a 30-amp junction box instead of connecting it into a socket, especially if there is no suitable socket near

where you want your new socket to be. In this case all you have to do is to locate the circuit cable run and pick a convenient point at which to make the connection.

If you have surface-run wiring, simply mount a rectangular white three-terminal junction box next to the cable run. Then switch off the power, cut the circuit cable and connect the cores to the terminals, live to live, neutral to neutral and earth to earth. Mount the new socket, run the spur cable from the new socket position back to the junction box and connect its cores to match those of the circuit cable. Fit the junction box cover and restore the power.

With concealed wiring, you have to lift floorboards to locate the circuit cable. Fit a round 30-amp three-terminal box to the side of a joist next to the cable, turn off the power and cut the cable. Reconnect the cores, plus those of the spur cable, fit the lid and replace the floorboards.

Direct connection

The third option for adding a socket is to locate the circuit cable, cut it and link the cut ends at the new socket. As mentioned earlier you can do this only if there is sufficient slack on the circuit cables where they lie beneath the floor. If there is, simply draw the cable up to the socket position, double it over and pass it into the mounting box. Turn the power off, cut through the cable and prepare the cores for connection to the new socket faceplate.

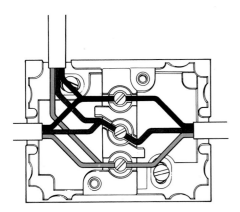

Above: Use a 30-amp three-terminal junction box to connect your spur cable to an existing ring or radial circuit cable.

MOVING A SOCKET

As your requirements for power points change, or you alter the way you furnish your home, you may find you have socket outlets that are in inconvenient or inaccessible positions – behind newly built-in cupboards, for example, or behind a heavy piece of furniture. If you already have ample outlets in the room, you can simply abandon such a socket, but if you need it and cannot reach it easily, one solution is to move it to a more accessible location. In fact, what you are doing is to run a spur from the existing socket position, which effectively becomes a junction box, to where the socket itself will be resited. All you need for the job is a new mounting box for the socket, a blanking-off plate for the existing mounting box, some cable and some 30-amp block connectors.

Start by deciding on the best position in the room for the socket, and fit the new mounting box at that point. Run the spur cable back from this to the old socket position, either surface-mounting it or passing it underneath the floorboards if its route runs parallel to the joists. Turn off the power to the circuit supplying the old socket, unscrew its faceplate and pull it away from the mounting box so you can disconnect the cable cores.

Reconnect the socket faceplate to the spur cable at the new socket position, and reattach the faceplate. Return to the old socket position and connect the spur and circuit cable cores together using three strip connectors. Link live to live, neutral to neutral and earth to earth. Press the cables and the connectors back into the old mounting box, and fit the blanking-off plate to the box.

If at any time in the future you want to bring the old socket back into use, simply remove the blanking plate, disconnect the cables from the block connectors and reconnect them to a socket faceplate. Remember that, depending on the original status of the socket, you may not be able to retain the spur you originally added to it. Unless the socket was originally on a ring or radial circuit, it cannot supply a spur and you will have to find an alternative connection point for the third cable.

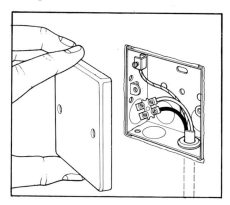

Above: *If an existing socket will be redundant, remove the faceplate, connect the cores to a block connector and fit a blanking-off plate to the box.*

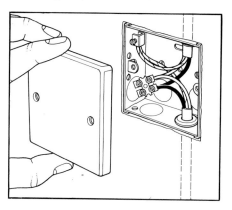

Above: *You could use a redundant socket as a junction box from where a spur can be run to a new socket position. Connect the old and new cables as shown.*

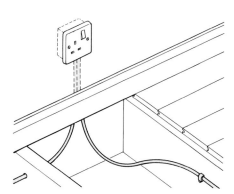

Above: *You can do away with an unwanted socket. Disconnect the cables supplying it and draw them back into the underfloor void.*

You can of course use this same technique to supply a new socket in an adjacent room, simply by drilling a hole through the wall behind the existing socket and feeding the spur cable through to the new socket.

Temporary sockets

If you need extra socket outlets for a short period and do not want to go to the trouble and expense of wiring them in, an acceptable alternative is to use a trailing socket. This allows you to plug up to four appliances into the socket, which in turn gets its power supply by being plugged into an existing outlet. For safety, screw the base of the trailing socket to the skirting board, and clip the flex to it so it is not a trip hazard. Take care not to overload the socket with appliances taking high currents such as heaters.

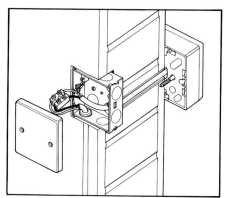

Above: *The simplest spur to run passes through the wall behind the redundant socket to a new socket mounted back-to-back. This involves minimal disruption.*

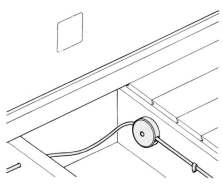

Above: *Remove the old box and make good. Reconnect the ends of the circuit cable at a 30-amp three-terminal junction box fixed to the side of a nearby joist.*

RESIDUAL CURRENT DEVICES

Fuses and MCBs provide protection against such faults as short circuits and overloading, but essentially they are to protect the circuitry rather than the user. However, there is a device designed to guard the user against the risks of receiving an electric shock as a result of a fault on the system (or user carelessness). It is called a residual current device (RCD), which used to be known as an earth-leakage circuit breaker or ELCB, and it works by detecting any imbalance between the current flowing out along the live wire of a circuit and the current flowing back along the neutral. Such an imbalance occurs if current leaks to earth; the two likeliest instances are when insulation breaks down (a fault which can cause an electrical fire) and when you touch a live part and current flows through your body to earth, giving you a shock.

A mild shock may do no more than tingle your fingers, but a severe shock can kill you, by interrupting and eventually stopping your heartbeat. When an RCD detects a current imbalance, it shuts off the current almost instantaneously – fast enough to prevent a fatal shock.

You can provide RCD protection to all or just part of your wiring installation. Many new homes now have a consumer unit that includes

Left: *Socket outlets incorporating an RCD are available in single and double versions, for indoor and outdoor use. Most fit on a standard-depth double-socket box, but some need a deeper one, so check before you buy. You can add one as a spur to existing wiring, or fit one to replace a double socket outlet.*

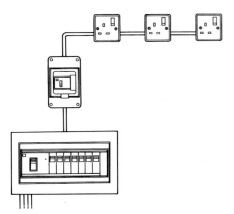

Above: *To provide protection for a whole circuit, wire the RCD into the circuit between the consumer unit and the first socket.*

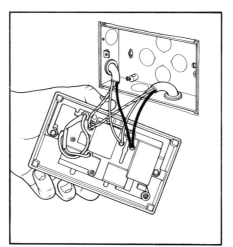

Above: *To fit an RCD socket in place of an existing double socket, disconnect the cable cores and link them to the RCD socket.*

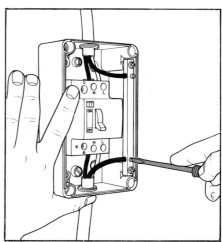

Above: *Install whole-circuit or whole-house RCDs in their own enclosures. The earth cores are wired to a connector bar.*

an RCD to protect every circuit in the house, but it is a simpler matter to install one alongside an existing consumer unit to give the system this valuable added protection. Alternatively, you can wire one into an individual circuit cable, for example to protect all socket outlets on that circuit.

Whether one is present or not, wiring regulations now require RCD protection for sockets used to power appliances for outdoor use such as lawn-mowers and hedgetrimmers. To meet this requirement, you can either fit an RCD to protect the circuit supplying the sockets you use for powering outdoor equipment, or you can designate a particular socket for outdoor use and fit a socket containing an RCD.

RCD socket outlets

These protected socket outlets are designed to fit a standard double-socket mounting box, so to convert an existing socket you simply remove the old double-socket faceplate and replace it with the RCD socket outlet, connecting the circuit cable cores to the L, N and E terminals as usual. You can alternatively add an RCD socket outlet to an existing circuit, wiring it up as a spur.

Wiring in an RCD

Separate RCDs come with their own mounting enclosure, and the incoming live and neutral cable cores are connected to terminals on the RCD. The earth core bypasses the RCD altogether; the cores are linked with a connector block.

FITTING AN ELECTRIC WALL HEATER

Wall-mounted electric heaters are a popular source of space heating, especially in bathrooms and bedrooms where additional heating is often required over and above that provided by central heating radiators. There are many different models available, but they fall into three main groups: radiant heaters, convector heaters and panel heaters. Radiant heaters have an element which glows visibly, backed by a reflector which directs the heat into the room. Convector heaters contain a fan which passes air over a bank of heating elements and out into the room. Panel heaters have the element sealed within a flat casing like a conventional water-filled radiator, or within tubes in the case of a towel rail; the casing or tubing contains oil which is heated by the element. All three types come in a wide range of designs, shapes and sizes, with output wattages ranging from 500W to 3kW (the maximum appliance rating that can be connected to a socket outlet).

While any of these heaters can be hung on a wall and simply plugged into a nearby socket outlet, it makes sense to give them their own permanent wiring connection. The simplest way of doing this is to connect a spur into an existing power circuit at a nearby socket or via a 30-amp junction box, and to run this spur in 2.5mm² cable to a switched fuse connection unit located close to the heater position. You then connect the spur cable cores to the set of terminals on the back of the faceplate marked FEED.

Next, pass the flex leading to the heater itself through the hole in the FCU faceplate, and connect its cores to the terminals marked LOAD. Make sure that the flex is secured by the cord grip on the back of the FCU faceplate, so that any pull on it will not strain the connections to the terminals and cause a potential short circuit.

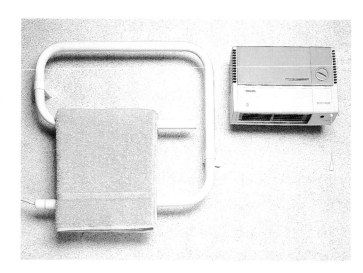

Right: Electric wall heaters are a versatile means of providing back-up heating in rooms such as bathrooms, WCs and poorly-heated bedrooms. Towel rails (left) and fan convector heaters (right) are two of the most popular types.

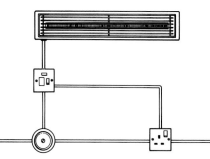

Above: Give electric heaters their own power supply via a spur, taken either from a 30-amp junction box or a socket and run to a fused connection unit fitted with a 13-amp fuse.

The FCU should be the switched type, allowing the heater to be isolated safely from the mains for cleaning or for maintenance tasks such as fitting new elements, and it is a good idea to fit one with a neon indicator as well, to show at a glance whether the power supply to the heater is on. The fuse in the FCU should be rated at 3 amps for heaters below 720 watts, and at 13 amps otherwise.

Where the heater is mounted in a bathroom, the fused connection unit must be out of reach of anyone using the bath or shower – in theory, it must be at least 2m (6 ft 6 in) away. This is impossible to achieve in a small bathroom, so to satisfy the requirements of the wiring regulations in this case the FCU is sited outside the bathroom and a further length of 2.5mm² cable is run from it to an accessory called a flex outlet, into which the flex from the heater is then connected through a hole in the faceplate. This outlet is the same size as the FCU and fits a standard single mounting box. Its faceplate has two sets of terminals: one for the incoming cable cores and the other for the outgoing flex cores. It is unswitched, so the FCU still provides the isolating switch for the heater itself.

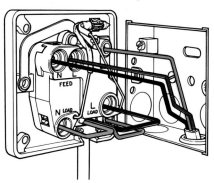

Above: Use a fused unit to supply power to the wall heater via a spur.

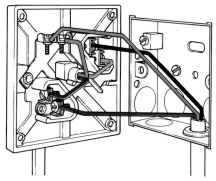

Above: Connect heater flex and supply cable within a flex outlet.

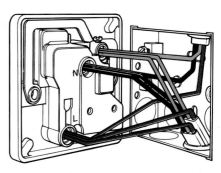

Left: Waste disposal units come in a range of sizes and can be adapted to fit both 38mm and 90mm sink outlets. The cutaway (centre) shows the grinding mechanism within the unit.

Below: Provide power for the waste disposal unit via a fused connection unit mounted underneath the sink and supplied by a spur cable from a nearby ring-circuit socket.

Above: Run the spur cable to the feed terminals of the FCU, and run flex on from the load terminals to the waste disposal unit.

Below: Supply the FCU via a spur cable connected to a nearby ring-circuit socket outlet.

FITTING A WASTE DISPOSAL UNIT

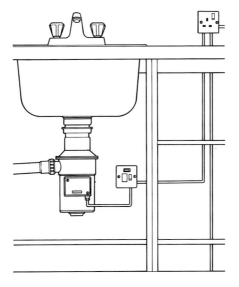

Waste disposal units are an increasingly popular feature in modern fitted kitchens as a means of disposing of kitchen waste quickly and hygienically. They can be fitted to most sinks, and are at their most useful where you have two separate bowls, allowing you to wash up at one bowl and dispose of waste at the other. All modern sinks with a 90mm (3½ in) waste outlet will accept the unit directly; on older sinks with 38mm (1½ in) diameter outlets you can either enlarge the hole or fit a special small-outlet adaptor which does not reduce the efficiency of the machine but does make it a little more difficult to feed in bulky waste material.

A waste disposal unit is basically a macerator, with a motor driving blades that reduce waste matter to a slurry; this is then washed into the waste system and on to the drains. The unit is protected by automatic cut-outs to prevent overloading or to shut off the blades if they become jammed with foreign objects.

On most units, the grinder is activated by a wall-mounted switch fitted near the sink, although some more sophisticated units switch on

automatically when the grinding compartment receives a full load and a supply of running water.

You can power your waste disposal unit simply by plugging it into any switched socket outlet. However, this is likely to be inconvenient even if you have a socket below worktop height and near the unit, since you will have to reach into the cupboard to switch on the unit every time you want to use it. It is better to wire the unit up with its own power supply and switch control.

If a wall-mounted switch is provided with the unit, the electrical arrangement is as follows. Run a

spur in 2.5mm² cable to a fused connection unit below worktop level. This need not be switched so long as the control switch is the double-pole type, and should contain a 13-amp fuse. Run cable up to the switch above the worktop, and back down to a flex outlet next to the waste disposal unit. Connect in the unit's flex at this point.

If no switch is provided, you can use a switched fused connection unit to provide both the power and the on/off control. Run a spur as before from a nearby circuit to the FCU but site it conveniently near the sink above worktop level. Connect the cable into the FEED terminals, run a further length of cable from the load terminals down to a flex outlet near the waste disposal unit itself, then connect in the flex cores. Alternatively, if you do not mind having the flex exposed between the FCU and the waste disposal unit, fit an FCU with a front or bottom flex outlet and run the flex direct from there to the waste disposal unit.

FITTING EXTRACTOR FANS

In modern well-insulated and draughtproofed homes, condensation can be a serious problem, especially in rooms such as kitchens and bathrooms where cooking and washing generate large amounts of water vapour. The most efficient means of getting rid of this is to discharge it direct to the outside air and to do this you need to install an extractor fan.

The commonest type is the rotary fan – a large propeller housed within a casing that draws air through an opening in a window pane, a wall or the ceiling. Other types have a cylindrical impeller like a fan heater. Both can discharge directly to the outside if mounted on an exterior wall, or can be connected to ducting.

Cooker hoods are fans designed to be mounted directly over the cooker, and usually incorporate a light as well; if you prefer this to a conventional fan in your kitchen, be sure to choose an extractor type; recirculators simply filter out grease and odours, but do not remove moisture.

The fan you choose should be powerful enough to change the air in the room at least six times an hour, and preferably more to cope with periods of excessive water vapour production. So work out the room volume and check with manufacturers' literature first.

If your extractor fan has an integral on/off pullcord, all you need to do to provide a power supply is to run a spur from a nearby circuit directly into the fan's terminals. Since fans are low-wattage appliances, the spur can be run from a loop-in rose or a junction box on a lighting circuit if this is convenient. Alternatively, you can take a fused spur from a power circuit, run it to an unswitched fused connection unit fitted next to the fan, and then connect the fan to it with a short length of flex.

If the fan does not have its own switch, you have two choices. You can take your spur cable to a switched fused connection unit mounted at a convenient position in the room (or outside it in the case of a bathroom if the FCU would be within reach of bath or shower), and then run cable on to a flex outlet next to the fan position. Or, wire the spur cable for the fan into the circuit supplying the room light, and add a wall- or ceiling-mounted switch to control it.

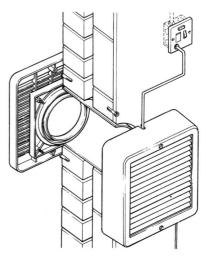

Above: Where the fan is installed in a solid cavity wall, line the hole with ducting and mount fan and grille directly on the walls.

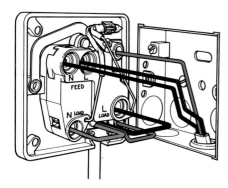

Above: Where the fan has its own cord on/off switch, provide a power supply via a spur feeding a fused connection unit.

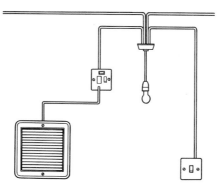

Above: Alternatively, supply the fan via a spur from a loop-in rose. Run the spur to an FCU, which also acts as the switch.

Above: Connect the cores of the incoming spur cable to the feed terminals, and wire the flex for the fan to the load terminals.

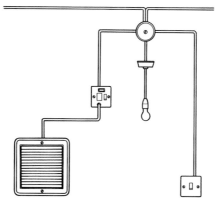

Above: A third option is to wire the fan via a four-terminal junction box so the room light also switches the fan on and off.

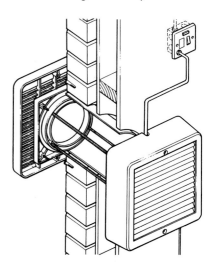

Above: In timber-framed houses, again fit ducting to prevent condensation in the cavity. Link fan and grille with metal straps.

FITTING SHAVER SOCKETS

Electric shavers need special sockets to accept the two-pin plug with which they are fitted. You can buy shaver adaptors which plug into socket outlets, but the socket outlets in most bedrooms are at skirting-board level, resulting in a very awkward shaving position, and ordinary socket outlets are not allowed in bathrooms anyway. The solution is to install tailor-made shaver sockets.

If you shave in a bathroom or washroom, you must install what is known as a shaver supply unit. This contains a transformer that provides an earth-free supply of current to the shaver; this means that the user is physically completely isolated from the mains, and cannot receive an electric shock. Such units generally offer a choice of two output voltages – 110V and 240V – so they can be used by visitors from countries on lower mains voltages. To select the voltage you either flick a switch or select two from a choice of three sockets for the plug. Shaver supply units also contain a self-resetting overload device which restricts the power supply to about 20W, so no other appliance can be plugged into the socket without causing the overload device to trip.

In other rooms you can install a shaver socket outlet, a special socket the same size as a single 13-amp socket outlet. This does not contain a transformer, so it is much cheaper and ideal for use in bedrooms, but does have a low-amperage fuse fitted in a fuseholder instead.

Both types are also available combined with a strip light, operated by a pull cord. Make sure you use the correct version in a bathroom.

You can supply power to a shaver supply unit or socket outlet as a spur taken directly from either a power or lighting circuit. In the case of a spur from a power circuit the cable is run to a fused connection unit fitted with a 3-amp fuse first, before being taken on to supply unit or socket.

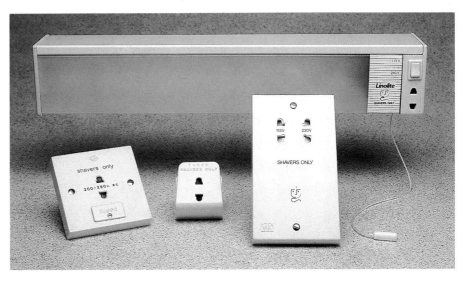

Above: A shaver light (top) provides light and a safe earth-free supply. Shaver sockets (bottom left) can be used anywhere except in bathrooms and washrooms, where a shaver supply unit (right) must be fitted. Shaver adaptors (centre) fit any 13-amp socket.

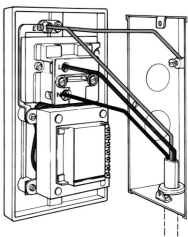

Right: The wiring within a shaver supply unit (top) and shaver socket (bottom).

Option 1 (below left): You can supply the shaver unit via a 1.0mm^2 spur run from a loop-in ceiling rose.

Option 2 (below left): Take a 2.5mm^2 spur to the shaver unit from a conveniently-sited socket outlet on a ring or radial circuit.

Option 3 (below right): Run a spur to the unit from a 5-amp three-terminal junction box cut into a nearby lighting circuit.

Option 4 (below right): If there is no convenient socket available for a spur connection, use a 30-amp junction box.

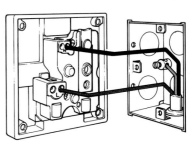

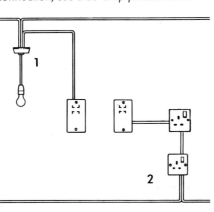

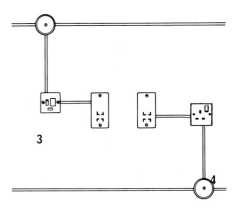

WIRING FOR CLOCKS

However good modern batteries are, they need replacing eventually, but a mains-operated clock never needs new batteries and costs virtually nothing to run. As with other appliances, you can supply the power simply by plugging the clock into a conveniently sited socket outlet, but this will mean having a long flex trailing up to the clock position, and also takes a socket outlet permanently out of use for other appliances.

A better – and far neater – solution is to run a spur cable from a convenient connection point on a nearby power or lighting circuit, and connect it to a wiring accessory called a clock connector. This is a specially designed plug and socket, with the plug actually recessed flush with the outlet's faceplate. The small square plug contains a 2-amp fuse, and is secured within its recess

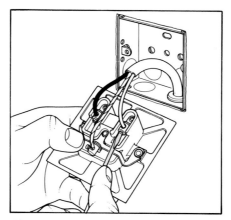

Above: Run a spur cable from a nearby lighting or power circuit and connect it to the terminals on the clock connector.

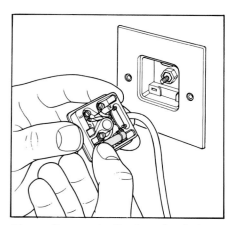

Above: Connect the flex from the clock to the plug-in part of the unit, fit a 2-amp fuse and secure the plug to the faceplate.

by a central screw.

The spur cable is connected to the L, N and E terminals on the back of the outlet faceplate, which fits a standard single socket mounting box. The flex from the clock is then passed through the opening in the plug faceplate and its cores are secured to the plug terminals.

If the flex between clock and plug is cut short and the clock connector is sited at the point where the clock will be positioned on the wall, the electrical connections can be effectively hidden once the clock is hung.

Clock connectors can also be used to power small appliances such as mains-operated radios.

WIRING UP CENTRAL HEATING CONTROLS

Modern central heating systems have much more sophisticated controls than their more primitive predecessors. At the heart of the system is the programmer, the most advanced of which allows the setting up of different periods of heating and hot water generation for each day of the week, as well as the allocation of space heating to different zones in the house by means of motorized valves. The programmer is linked to the boiler and the system's circulating pump, and their operation is also controlled by the room thermostat, monitoring the air temperature, and by the cylinder thermostat which checks the temperature of water stored in the hot cylinder. There may even be an exterior froststat which will override other controls and bring the system into operation in very cold weather.

The positioning of these various controls will be dictated by the layout of your central heating system – see diagram opposite. Some obvious-

ly have fixed positions: the cylinder thermostat, for example, is attached to the hot water cylinder, and thermostatic radiator valves go on the radiators they control. Similarly, the positions of motorized valves will depend on the pipework layout, although it is a good idea to ensure that you have easy access to both valves and pump in case you need to repair or replace them in the future.

You have much greater flexibility over where you place the controller and the room thermostat. The controller should be sited somewhere convenient such as in the hall, kitchen or living room, while the room thermostat should be positioned away from cold draughts and heat sources such as radiators. Since you are likely to spend most time in the living room, it is probably best to place it there so that the temperature in that room is the temperature set. Lastly, the froststat should be sited on an outside wall, shielded from the prevailing winter winds.

On a typical system, all these controls are wired together via a multi-terminal junction box, and the precise details of the connections to be made will vary according to what equipment is being used. Controls of all types come complete with detailed wiring instructions, and you should follow these to the letter when wiring up your system.

The one connection that is common to all wiring arrangements is an incoming power supply, which is taken to the multi-terminal junction box that links the various controls together. You can provide this supply as a spur, from either a lighting circuit or a power circuit, whichever is more convenient. However, in both cases the spur cable should run to a switched fuse connection unit, so that you can cut off the power to the system if you need to do repair or maintenance work on it. Then 1.0mm² cable is used to link the connection unit to the multi-terminal junction box.

Right: (*1*) A thermostatic radiator valve allows control of the heat output of individual radiators. (*2*) A motorized valve diverts water to the heating system or the hot cylinder as required. (*3*) A junction box links all the controls together. (*4*) A room thermostat is used to set the system's operating temperature, while (*5*) a programmer controls its operating periods. (*6*) A cylinder stat keeps hot water at a safe temperature, while (*7*) a froststat brings the heating on when outside temperatures fall.

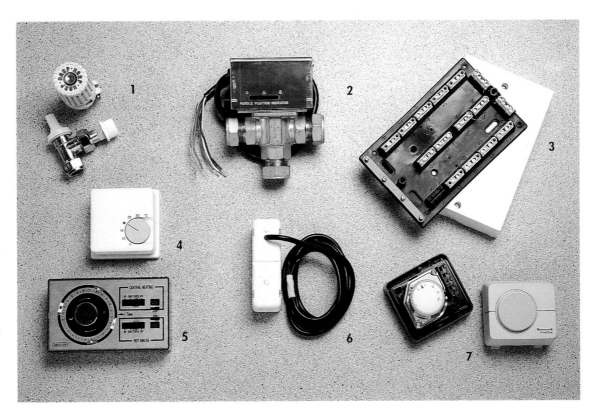

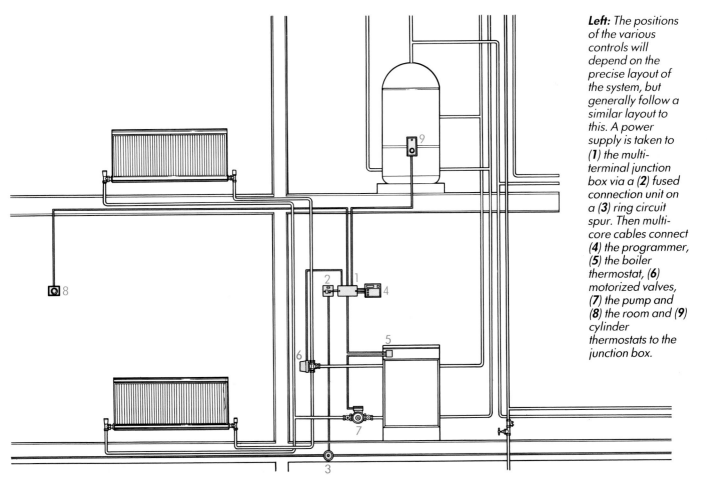

Left: The positions of the various controls will depend on the precise layout of the system, but generally follow a similar layout to this. A power supply is taken to (*1*) the multi-terminal junction box via a (*2*) fused connection unit on a (*3*) ring circuit spur. Then multi-core cables connect (*4*) the programmer, (*5*) the boiler thermostat, (*6*) motorized valves, (*7*) the pump and (*8*) the room and (*9*) cylinder thermostats to the junction box.

TV AND FM OUTLETS

Unless you are fortunate enough to live close to your local transmitters, you will probably need rooftop or loft aerials to provide a good signal for TV and for FM radio reception. Coaxial cable is then run down inside the house to supply aerial socket outlets situated near your TV or hi-fi equipment. You can fit cable runs to supply separate sockets for TV and FM reception, or you can use special combined TV/FM diplexer sockets.

Start by mounting the first diplexer socket at a convenient point in the loft, and connect the leads from your TV and FM aerials into the front of the socket using standard coaxial plugs. Now connect a single length of coaxial cable to the terminals on the back of the socket, run it by a convenient route down through the house to your chosen socket outlet position, and connect it to a second socket. Finally, plug in the leads to your TV and radio.

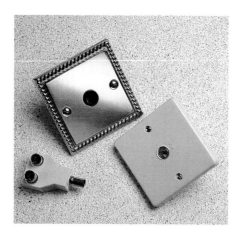

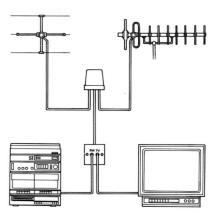

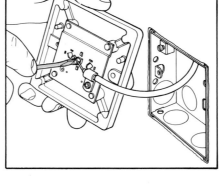

Above left: TV and FM socket outlets are available in a range of plastic and metal finishes to match other wiring accessories.

Above: If you have both TV and FM radio aerials on the roof or in the loft, you can avoid the need for two aerial downloads by using diplexers. One in the loft connects the aerial leads, and one download runs to the combined TV/FM socket outlet.

Left: Run the aerial download into the back of a flush or surface-mounted box, prepare the end of the coaxial cable and connect it to the terminals on the back of the faceplate.

BELL CIRCUITS

Battery-operated bell systems are extremely simple to wire up; all you have to do is link the bell push or pushes to the bell or chime unit using two-core bell wire, making the connections as specified in the fitting instructions. However, if you want an illuminated bell push, you will have to power your bell system from the mains, or the bulb in the bell push will soon drain the system's batteries. This means using a special bell transformer, which will provide a suitable low-voltage supply for the system.

You can simply plug the transformer into the mains at a convenient socket outlet, but it is a much better method to provide a permanent connection via a spur. This can be taken directly from a lighting or power circuit for your particular situation, whichever is the more convenient, but in either case the spur should run to a switched fused connection unit or a clock connector.

Right: With battery-operated bells, you simply link the bell housing (which usually contains the battery) to the bell push using two-core bell wire. If the bell is run from a transformer, it needs a power supply from a fused connection unit or a clock connector.

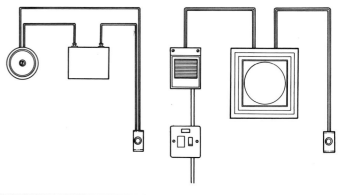

Right: Both battery and mains-operated bells are usually sold as complete kits; all you have to do is to simply follow the wiring instructions to connect everything up. You can choose bells, buzzers or chimes, and there is a wide range of casing designs and finishes available to choose from.

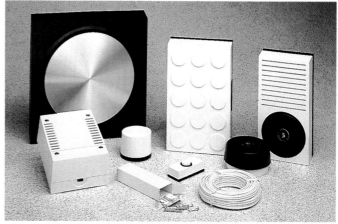

PHONE SOCKETS

Since 1986 householders have been allowed to wire up as many as three extension phones to their existing phone line, using easily-available phone extension kits. To do so, you need a line terminating with a modern, square master socket; if you have the older-style connection box, British Telecom will fit a new master socket free of charge.

Extension kits contain a plug-in converter which you fit into the master socket, plus about 15m (50ft) of special six-core cable and an extension socket. You can buy additional sockets and cable, plus junction boxes if the layout of your home demands a branching system rather than a series one.

Wiring up the extension sockets is simplicity itself. You run the cable along the tops of skirtings, over door architraves or under floorboards to the new socket position, and connect the six cores to their terminals using the special tool in the kit.

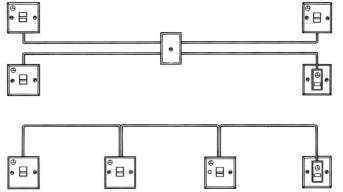

Left: You can run the cable from the master socket to a joint box and then take branches to several phone positions.

Left: Alternatively, loop the cable from one phone to the next in series . . . up to a maximum of four.

Right: A typical phone extension kit contains a length of multi-core cable (sometimes with a plug-in converter attached), an extension socket, a box of cable clips and a special tool for inserting the cable cores into the terminals on the extension socket.

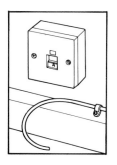 

Above: Decide where you want your extension socket, and screw it to the wall. Then run the cable to it, leaving plenty of slack.

Above right: Slit the cable sheath carefully with a knife so you can find the drawstring.

Below: Ease the drawstring out, wrap it round your fingers and pull it along the cable to split the sheath. Cut off the waste.

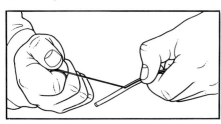

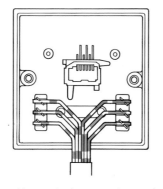

Above: At the extension socket, connect the six cores as shown. White cores with coloured rings go to the left, coloured cores with white rings to the right.

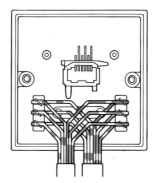

Above: At intermediate sockets, add the second set of wires in the same order as the first. In junction boxes, connect two cables at one set of terminals, two at the other.

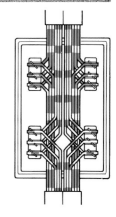

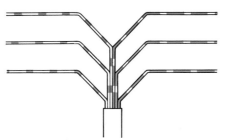

Left: Three of the six cores are white with coloured rings, three are coloured with white rings.

Right: Extension kits should contain a special tool for connecting cores to terminals.

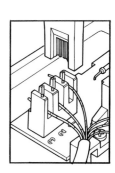

FITTING
BURGLAR ALARMS

With the relentless rise in burglaries, more and more home owners are looking for better security to protect their homes and their possessions. Good locks are part of the battle, but there is nothing like a full-scale burglar alarm system for providing an additional deterrent for a would-be burglar as well as peace of mind for the home owner.

Most domestic burglar alarm systems consist of three main components: detectors, the control unit and the alarm itself, usually connected by thin flex. There are various types of detectors, which are basically small electrical switches which break the continuity of the circuit if they are disturbed. These are fitted to doors and windows, either mounted on the surface or recessed into them, so that unauthorized entry at these points breaks the circuit. They are also used in pressure mats, which are placed under carpets to detect movement within the home if the intruder defeats the door and window sensors. Any break in circuit continuity is detected by the system's main control unit, which then either sounds an audible alarm on the outside of the house or initi-

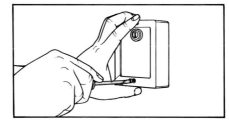

1 Mount the main alarm control unit at a point near your front door.

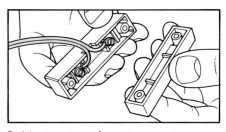

2 Most systems have two-part sensors for protecting doors and windows.

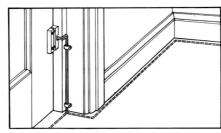

3 Mount the sensors on vulnerable doors and windows, and conceal the circuit cables round the room.

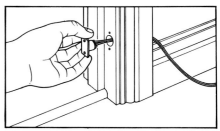

4 Some systems have sensors designed to be recessed into door and window frames.

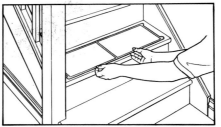

5 Fit pressure pads on traffic routes such as the stairs. Place them on an upper tread to trick intruders.

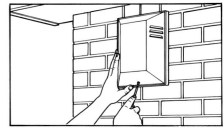

6 Mount the alarm high on the house wall in a visible position. Run the cables through the wall behind it.

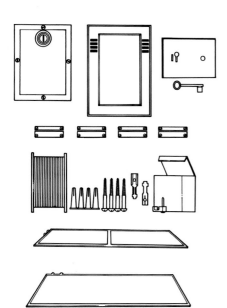

Left: Typical burglar alarm kits for DIY installation contain all the components you are likely to need – the main control unit, sensors, pressure pads, cable and clips plus the external alarm.

Right: The basic wiring arrangement is similar on all systems. Sensors are wired up like ringmain power circuits, while other components are linked directly to the control unit.

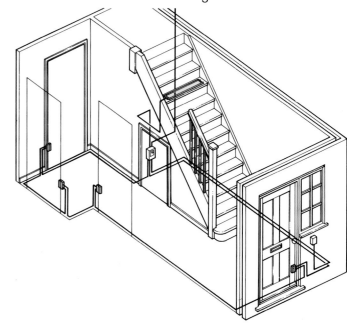

ates an automatic telephone call to a central monitoring station.

Movement detectors are more versatile devices, reacting to any movement within their fields of view inside the home.

Microwave and ultrasonic detectors send out signals and pick up the echoes; these are disturbed if an intruder is present, and the alarm is then sounded. Passive infra-red detectors read the pattern of infra-red radiation within their field of view, and sense the body heat of anyone moving within range, again triggering the alarm.

Break-glass detectors are useful for protecting large areas of fixed glass. One type consists of thin metallic foil which is stuck round the perimeter of the window. Breaking the glass breaks the foil, opens an electric contact and sets off the alarm. Vibration detectors sense the impact of the window breaking.

Personal attack buttons are simple push-to-operate switches which allow you to activate the alarm if you are inside the house and sense that someone has gained admittance or are confronted with someone forcing their way in when you open the door. It is best to site them by exterior doors and by your bedside.

The control unit is the heart of the system, and its main function is to receive signals from the various detectors, to monitor all the circuits and to sound the alarm. It also provides a power supply for the whole system, and may include provision for dividing the house into two or more zones which are protected individually. It features indicators to show you the status of the system, and of course the master on/off settings.

Most also incorporate protection from tampering in the form of a microswitch which sets off the alarm if anyone tries to prise open the unit and cut off the power.

Most systems use mains and battery power, switching over to rechargeable batteries if there is a power failure. The power is supplied via a fused spur.

Wireless systems

Some burglar alarm systems now use the home's electrical circuits to carry signals from the various detectors. These are generally movement or PIR detectors, which are plugged into sockets in each room. Signals are then transmitted via the mains wiring to a control unit plugged in elsewhere in the home and linked to an alarm on an external wall of the house or to an automatic telephone dialling unit. The advantage of this type of system is that there is no tedious wiring work to carry out; everything simply plugs into existing socket outlets.

Even more sophisticated is the system illustrated below. This uses low-powered radio transmitters as the signalling device, so once again there are no wires to install. Conventional types of detector are used, but each one is connected to its own small radio transmitter which sends coded digital signals to a receiver mounted in the portable control panel. This in turn communicates with an alarm on the outside of the house or to a central monitoring station. Magnetic detectors can be fitted to protect doors and windows, while PIR movement sensors protect whole rooms or remote outbuildings. Panic buttons can be added to the system at any convenient point.

The other major advantage of wireless systems is that you can 'unplug' them and take them with you when you move home.

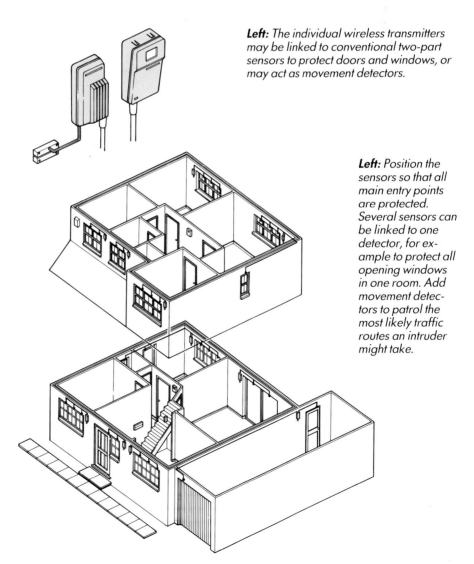

Left: *The individual wireless transmitters may be linked to conventional two-part sensors to protect doors and windows, or may act as movement detectors.*

Left: *Position the sensors so that all main entry points are protected. Several sensors can be linked to one detector, for example to protect all opening windows in one room. Add movement detectors to patrol the most likely traffic routes an intruder might take.*

WORK ON NEW CIRCUITS

There is a limit to what you can do simply by adding to your existing home wiring. The circuits may have reached their current-carrying capacity, or may not run where you want them. What you need is extra circuits – perhaps to bring light and power to a home extension, or to supply a powerful new appliance such as an instantaneous shower. If this is the case, you must be prepared for rather more extensive work than is involved when you add to existing circuits. However, adding extra circuits does give you the opportunity to bring your home's wiring up to the standard you need – even many brand new homes still do not make enough provision for the number of electrical appliances used in the home nowadays. It also gives you the chance to improve the electrical protection your system provides – both for itself, and also for the safety of you and your family.

If you live in a new home or one that has been recently rewired, you may have a consumer unit with one or more spare fuseways. If so, you will see spaces in the consumer unit occupied by plain blanking-off plates. All you have to do is to replace these with fuseholders or MCBs of the right rating for the type of circuit you plan to install, and then run in the circuit cable.

Your first step is to turn off the system's main isolating switch or RCD. You can then open the consumer unit to gain access to the busbar on which the fuseholders or MCBs are mounted. Remove the blanking-off plate(s) so you can insert the new fuseholder/MCB. Make sure you fit one with the correct rating for the circuit you plan to install. The fuseholder or MCB with the highest current rating should be nearest to the on/off switch, so you may have to move existing ones along the busbar to enable you to insert the new one in the right place in the sequence.

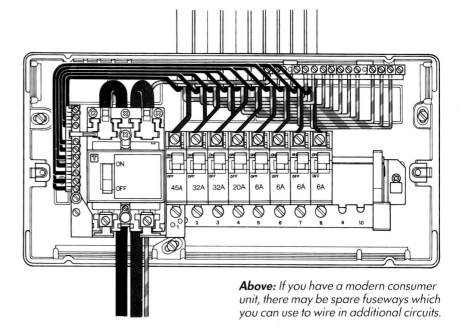

Above: If you have a modern consumer unit, there may be spare fuseways which you can use to wire in additional circuits.

Now attach the live core of your new circuit cable to the terminal on the new fuseholder or MCB, and link the neutral core to the unit's main neutral terminal block. Finally, sleeve the bare earth core of the new circuit cable in green/yellow PVC sleeving and link it to the unit's main earth terminal block. Make sure that the new circuit cable runs neatly out of the unit, fit the cover and restore the power.

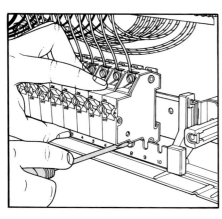

1 If possible, make room for the new MCB by sliding existing ones along the main busbar.

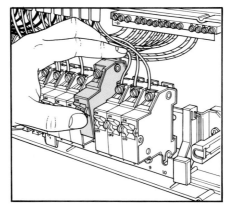

2 Insert the new MCB in the space. Check that the highest-rated MCBs are nearest to the on/off switch or RCD.

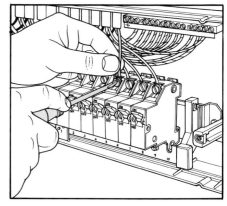

3 Connect the live core to its MCB, and link the neutral and earth cores to their terminal blocks.

ADDING A NEW SWITCHFUSE UNIT

Few homes will have spare fuseways from which new circuits can be run. For most people, adding extra circuits means installing an extra unit called a switchfuse unit alongside the existing consumer unit to provide the additional circuit fuseways that you require.

Choose a new unit not only to provide the extra circuits you need now, but also to cope with any more circuits you might want to add in the future. You can buy units containing one, two, four, six, nine or even 12 fuseways, but for most homes a unit with four fuseways is likely to be the most common choice. Once it is installed, it will have its own power supply and will control the new circuits quite independently of the existing consumer unit.

When you have decided on the size of unit you need, you should then think about the circuit protection. Even if your existing unit contains rewirable or cartridge fuses, it is best to fit MCBs in your new one. They offer far better protection against overloading than fuses do, and are far more convenient to use. You can switch them off to isolate individual circuits for repairs or alterations, and in the event of a fault on the circuit they switch off the power automatically. There is no longer any need to repair blown fuses; you simply switch them on again after clearing the fault.

You should also think about including RCD protection for your new circuits, and this is essential to meet the requirements of the wiring regulations if the circuits will power appliances used out of doors. You can either incorporate an RCD in your new switchfuse unit (it takes the place of the isolating switch), or you can install it in a separate enclosure. In the former case, only the circuits running from the new switchfuse unit are protected by the RCD, but in the latter case you can reorganize the wiring so your entire

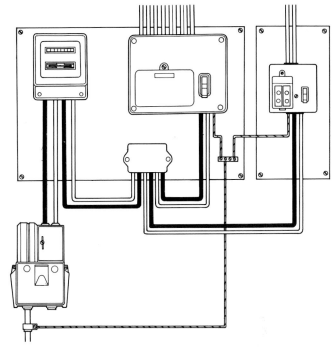

Right: If your system has no room for expansion, you will have to install an additional switchfuse unit to protect the new circuits. Its power supply must be taken from a new distribution box, and the existing fusebox must be supplied from this.

Below: Mount your new switchfuse unit next to the existing fusebox. Connect new supply cables to its terminals.

Below right: Run in the new circuit cables. Link cores to terminals as shown.

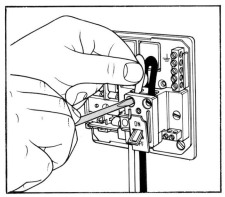

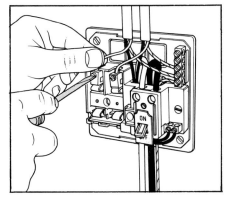

home is protected. See page 86 for more details.

To install the new unit, mount it alongside or close to the existing consumer unit. Fit the MCBs you require into it, and run in the new circuit cables. Complete the wiring of the new circuits, ready for the mains power to be connected.

To do this, you need what is called a service connector box. The electricity board – not you – then disconnects the main leads running from the meter to the existing consumer unit and reconnects them to the connector box. New leads are now run from the connector box to both the existing consumer unit and the new unit you have installed.

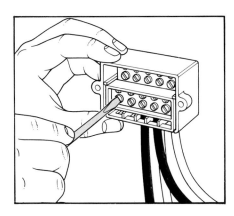

Above: Mount a new distribution box close to the existing fusebox, and connect in the supply cables to the new switchfuse unit. Then contact your local electricity board or a qualified electrician to come and reconnect the old fusebox.

WIRING UP A NEW LIGHTING CIRCUIT

If you want to wire up additional lights in your home and your existing light circuits are already supplying their practical maximum of eight lighting points, you need an additional circuit. This will be run from a new 5-amp fuseway – either in the consumer unit if a spare fuseway is available, or in a new switchfuse unit added alongside the existing one (see pages 72-73). The circuit is run in 1.0mm² two-core-and-earth cable, and you can use the loop-in or junction-box systems or a mixture of both to follow the easiest cable routes and make the most economical use of cable.

Start by planning the circuit on paper, so you can work out what wiring accessories you will need – loop-in ceiling roses and pendant lampholders, batten lampholders, ceiling or wall light fittings, wall- or ceiling-mounted light switches, junction and conduit boxes, terminal connector blocks and so on. Work out the routes the cables will take, starting at the consumer unit and running across floors or ceilings and up or down walls as appropriate, so you can estimate the amount of cable you will need. Add 10 per cent to the total to allow for errors or unforeseen problems.

When you have assembled all the equipment and the tools you will need, you can start work. The first step is to run the circuit cable from the consumer unit to the various

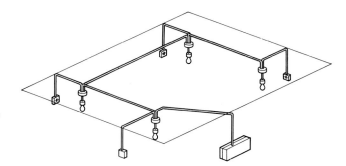

Left: *With loop-in wiring, the circuit cable runs directly from one light fitting to the next, and switch cables for each light are connected into the rose or fitting.*

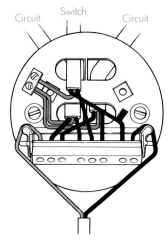

Above: *Intermediate roses on a loop-in system have both an incoming and outgoing circuit cable and a switch cable.*

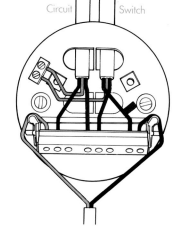

Above: *The final rose on the system has just two cables present – the incoming circuit cable and the switch cable.*

lighting positions. At the consumer unit and at each lighting position, leave a generous amount of cable to allow you to make connections easily before running the cable on to the next one.

If you are working in the loft, do not leave cables lying loose. Where they run parallel to the joists, clip them to the joist sides at 450mm (18 in) intervals, just below the top of the joist so they are not covered by loft insulation. Where you have to cross the line of the joists you *can* simply run the cable over the top of the joists, but it could be damaged if it is trodden on or if stored items are pushed over it. It is preferable to drill holes through the joists and pass the cable through.

For cable runs between floor and ceiling, you will have to lift floorboards to gain acccess to the ceiling void. Where the cable runs parallel to the joists, you should lift a board at each side of the room, feed the

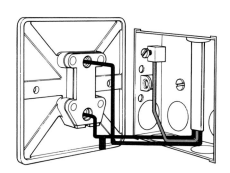

Above: *Each light fitting is controlled by its own switch. Use one-way switches with two terminals unless you want two-way switching.*

new cable through between them and simply leave it lying on the ceiling surface. Where the cable runs across the line of the joists, lift one line of boards across the room so you can thread the cable through holes drilled in the joists.

Now install the lights – either loop-in roses or individual fittings. Make sure that you mount them

Checklist

- Ceiling roses
- Pendant lampholders and flex
- Batten lampholders
- New light fittings
- Junction boxes
- Conduit boxes
- Light switches
- Connector blocks
- 1.0mm² cable

securely, either direct to the under-side of a joist or to a batten secured between them for ceiling fittings. Now connect the supply cables to them, either directly, if you are using the loop-in system, or from a nearby junction box. Mount junction boxes securely to the sides of joists or to battens set between the joists, and fit their covers securely when the wiring at each one is complete. Remember to sleeve all bare earth cores as you work.

If you are connecting the circuit cable directly to individual light fittings which have short flex tails, use terminal connectors to link the flex and cable cores, and ensure that these are enclosed in a conduit box behind the fitting's baseplate. For ceiling fittings, do not chisel away the underside of a joist so you can recess the box flush with the ceiling surface; instead, mount it beneath a batten fixed between the joists at the correct height to leave the lip of the box sitting flush with the ceiling surface below.

The next step is to carry out the switch wiring, taking cable from each light (on the loop-in system) or from its junction box down to the switch position. Channel out chases in the wall surfaces, and use the same two-core-and-earth cable for this as for the rest of the circuit wiring. If any two-way switching is involved, use 1.0mm² three-core-and-earth cable to link the individual two-way switches.

Now double-check that you have made all connections properly and that you have linked together all the components of the new circuit correctly. In particular, make sure that you have sleeved the earth continuity conductor wherever it is exposed, and that you have connected it to the right terminal at each point on the circuit.

You can now return to the consumer unit or switchfuse unit that will supply the circuit and connect up the circuit cable to its appropriate fuseway. Make sure the power to the unit is off, then connect the circuit cable's live core to the fuse-

Right: With a junction-box system, the circuit cable runs to a series of four-terminal junction boxes. From each of these one cable runs to the light position and another to the switch controlling the light.

Above: Make the connections in the four-terminal junction boxes as shown. Flag the black switch cable core with red PVC tape.

Above: Roses on junction-box systems have just one circuit cable present, connected to the rose terminals as shown.

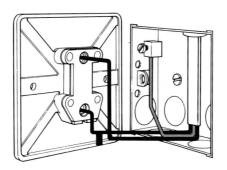

Above: As with loop-in wiring, use a one-way switch to control each light unless you want two-way switching arrangements.

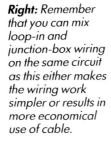

Right: Remember that you can mix loop-in and junction-box wiring on the same circuit as this either makes the wiring work simpler or results in more economical use of cable.

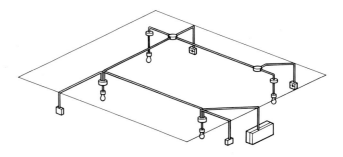

holder or MCB, the neutral to the unit's neutral terminal and the earth to the main earth terminal.

Before finally restoring the power to your new circuit by replacing the fuse or switching on the MCB, double-check the connections within the consumer unit. Then close up ceiling roses and pendant lamp-holders, check that switch faceplates are secure, and fit lamps of the appropriate wattages to your new fittings all round the circuit. Label the new fuseway and restore power to check that it all works.

WIRING UP
A NEW RING MAIN

The only restriction on the number of socket outlets an existing ring main circuit can supply is that the number of sockets on spurs must not exceed the number of sockets on the ring itself. This means that you are likely to be able to satisfy your requirements for extra socket outlets in the home simply by adding spurs. However, there is a restric-

tion on the floor area that one ring circuit can supply – a total of 100sq m (1075sq ft) is the limit – so if you are extending your home you will probably have to consider installing a completely new ring circuit to supply it.

To do this, you need a spare fuseway in your consumer unit; if you do not have one, you will need to add a switchfuse unit (see page 73). The circuit itself is protected by a 30-amp fuse or MCB, and is entirely run in 2.5mm² two-core-and-earth

cable. This loops from socket to socket round the ring, and can feed spurs taken from sockets on the ring or from 30-amp junction boxes as necessary. The circuit can also feed fused connection units if these are required for fixed appliances, and can supply fused spurs for items such as wall lights.

As with a new lighting circuit, the first stage is to plan exactly where you want the new circuit to surface – in other words, where you want socket outlets, fused connection

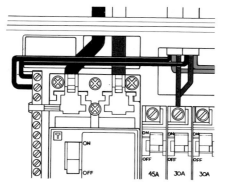

Right: Link the live cores of the two ring cables to the terminal of a 30-amp fuse or MCB. Take the neutral and earth cores to their own main terminal blocks.

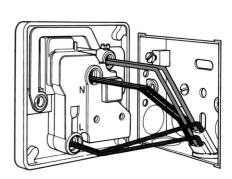

Right: Wire up sockets on the ring circuit as shown here, with live, neutral and earth cores connected to their labelled terminals on the back of the socket faceplate. Fit green/yellow PVC sleeving over the bare earth cores.

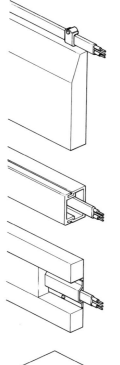

Left: You can surface-mount cables along skirting boards, conceal them in surface-mounted plastic mini-trunking or bury them in chases cut in the plaster, adding protective channelling if you wish. Where cables cross the lines of floor joists, pass them through holes drilled in the joist centres.

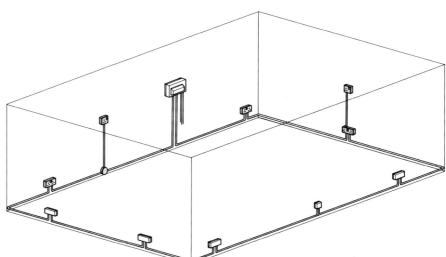

Right: The ring main circuit cable runs from socket to socket. Spurs may be connected at sockets or using 30-amp junction boxes.

Right: Fused connection units can be wired directly onto the ring circuit.

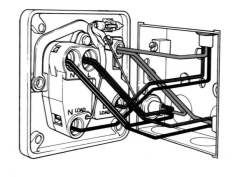

units and so on to be situated. This is usually dictated by the positions of the various appliances you intend to use, such as a hi-fi, hobby equipment, kitchen appliances, electric blankets and so on. Remember too that sockets do not have to be at skirting-board level; in certain circumstances it may be more convenient to site them higher up the wall, especially in rooms with built-in furniture.

When you have decided on the outlet positions, you can plan the cable route, taking into account the sort of wall and floor structure your home has. For example, if you have solid ground floors you may consider using some kind of surface-mounted trunking to conceal the wiring, or running the circuit cable in the void above the ground-floor ceiling with cable drops running down the wall to each socket. With stud partition walls, you may be able to conceal wiring within the partition.

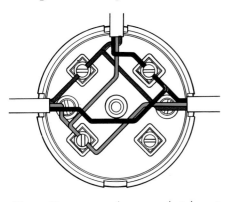

Above: You can supply spur sockets by cutting a 30-amp junction box into the circuit and connecting the cores as shown here.

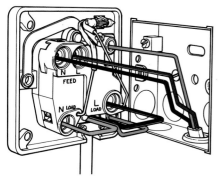

Above: Fused connection units on spurs also have just one supply cable present. Different types of FCU allow either flex or cable connections to be made.

Use this plan to decide which sockets and other accessories will be wired on the ring itself, and which will be fed as spurs from it. This enables you to estimate how much cable to buy for the job, as well as to calculate the number of wiring accessories needed.

As with installing new lighting circuits, it is best to begin by fitting

mounting boxes at all the outlet positions. These can be flush- or surface-mounted, depending on whether you have chosen concealed or surface-run wiring. If you are flush-mounting the cable and sockets, cut chases down to the floor or up to the ceiling for the supply cable to each outlet at the same time as you chop out the recesses for the boxes, so you have only one lot of clearing up and making good to do. Remember to remove knockouts from mounting boxes to provide a

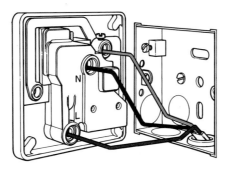

Above: Sockets on a spur have just a single cable present. The cores are linked to their terminals as for ring sockets. Remember that a spur can feed only one socket.

cable entry point before fitting them in place, and fit a rubber grommet in the knockout of metal boxes to prevent chafing of the cable sheathing.

Now you can start running in the circuit cable. Run the cable that will form one end of the ring from the consumer unit to the first outlet position and draw it up into the box. Leave enough surplus cable to allow for making the core connections at each point, and then take the cable on to the next one. Where spurs are to be included, run extra lengths of cable to them from their supply points (a ring socket or a 30-amp junction box). Finally, run the cable back from the last socket on the ring to the consumer unit.

When you have run in all the cables, you can connect individual outlets to it. At each outlet point, strip back the cable sheathing and the core insulation. Where there are two or more cables, twist like cable cores together to ensure good elec-

trical contact, and secure them in their terminals on the back of the accessory faceplates. Sleeve bare earth wires with green/yellow sleeving. Double-check that the connections are correct before fitting the accessory to its mounting box.

Complete the connection of all the outlets on the circuit. Now return to the consumer unit, turn off the power and connect the two cables to the terminals within the consumer unit or switchfuse unit. The two live cores are connected to the terminal on the fuseholder or MCB, while both neutrals and both earths go to the main neutral and earth terminals respectively. Again, sleeve the bare earth cores, then restore the power.

Options

Flush wiring If you are prepared for the extra work involved, the neatest way of wiring your new circuit is to conceal the cable beneath floors and in chases cut in wall surfaces.

Surface wiring Alternatively, clip cable to the tops of skirting boards, run it in mini-trunking or conceal it by using special skirting, architrave and cornice mouldings.

If you want flush wiring but do not want to disturb walls and ceilings until you next redecorate, use one of the surface-wiring options for now. Leave plenty of slack on the new cable runs so they can be flush-mounted in chases cut in the plaster.

Checklist

- Socket outlets
- Fused connection units
- Mounting boxes
  (flush or surface)
- Rubber grommets
- Green/yellow earth sleeving
- 30-amp junction boxes
- Cable clips
- Mini-trunking
- Skirting/architrave/cornice
  mouldings
- 2.5mm² cable

EXTENDING RING CIRCUITS

There is another way to supply additional socket outlets without the need for a completely new circuit, which involves breaking an existing ring circuit and connecting in new cable to extend it to another part of the home. You can do this either by disconnecting the existing ring circuit cable between two socket outlets and connecting the ends of the ring extension to them to form a larger ring, or by literally severing the circuit cable at a convenient point and using two 30-amp junction boxes to wire in the extension. You can use either of these methods to extend a circuit anywhere provided the total floor area of the rooms served by the extended circuit does not exceed the 100sq m (1075sq ft) limit allowed by the Wiring Regulations.

If you decide that this is a viable option, start by planning the positions of the new socket outlets which the extension will serve. Remember that, as with any ring circuit, some of the new sockets can be supplied as spurs by connecting them to sockets on the extension itself, or to 30-amp junction boxes on the extension. This will then help you to work out the best route for the extension to take – a decision which will then indicate the best points to break into the existing ring.

To add the extension, first install the mounting boxes for the new outlets, and cut any cable chases that are needed to reach them. You then run the cable from the point where it joins the existing ring, round to each socket in turn and then back to its other connection point. Leave enough cable at each point for making connections, and wire up each accessory in turn.

When all the new outlets are wired up and fitted to their mounting boxes, you can make the final connections to the existing ring. Turn off the power to the circuit and cut into or disconnect the existing circuit cable at your chosen point.

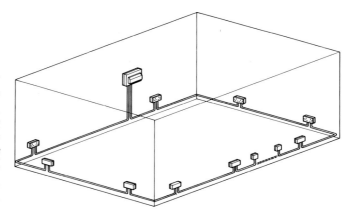

Left: The principle of extending a ring circuit involves breaking the existing ring and adding new cable to serve a larger floor area (up to 100 sq m maximum).

Now connect up the ends of the extension cable to complete the new enlarged ring circuit. You can connect the new cables to the existing ones in three ways. The first is to use a 30-amp junction box. The second is to make the connections at a socket outlet on the original ring at the point where you have decided to break it; simply link old and new cables at the socket terminals. The third is to use a socket on the original ring as a junction box, with connector blocks linking the cores.

Options

You can use this technique to take power to a new extension provided that the extended circuit is not required to serve rooms with a total floor area exceeding 100sq m (1075sq ft). The extension does not have to serve rooms on the same floor as the original circuit.

You can also use it to increase without limit the number of socket outlets in any room served by the original ring.

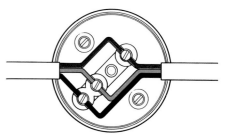

Above: You can connect the new and existing circuit cables within a 30-amp junction box.

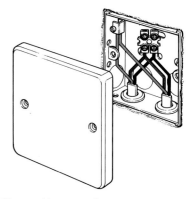

Above: Alternatively, use an existing socket as a junction box, linking the cables as shown and fitting a blanking plate.

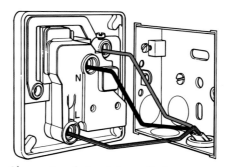

Above: A socket outlet supplied as a spur has just one cable. Wiring regulations stipulate that spurs may feed only one single or double socket outlet or one FCU.

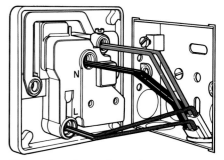

Above: A socket outlet on the main ring circuit has two cables. The cores should be twisted together in pairs as shown, or may be uncut and simply crimped to a U-shape.

SPLITTING CIRCUITS

Forming two rings

If you want to supply sockets in a new or unsupplied area of the home, you can use a variation on the technique of extending ring circuits described opposite even if the floor area served will exceed 100sq m (1075sq ft). The technique involves splitting an existing ring circuit into two halves, then running new cables back to the consumer unit from the point at which the circuit was severed. The effect of this is to create two new, smaller rings, each of which can then be extended if required, and often means far less upheaval in providing extra sockets than would be involved in adding a complete new circuit. However, it does mean you need a spare fuseway in your consumer unit, or a new switchfuse unit alongside it, to provide the extra circuit with a power supply.

Adding a switchfuse unit will involve far less upheaval and making good than actually wiring in a new circuit from scratch, and does give you the opportunity to provide extra fuseways for other purposes too.

The only thing to you have to decide when splitting a circuit in this way is where it will be most convenient to make the break.

One option is to break the existing ring by disconnecting the section of circuit cable between two adjacent ring sockets. Each ring is then completed by running new cable back from the socket concerned to the consumer unit; it is useful to remember that it can feed more new sockets on the way.

Another option available is to sever the ring circuit cable at some point where it runs beneath the floorboards, and to wire the cut ends into two 30-amp junction boxes. You then run new cable from each junction box back to the consumer unit as before. Use 2.5mm² two-core-and-earth cable for all the new wiring, and fit a 30-amp fuseholder or MCB to protect each of the two new circuits.

Forming two radials

A similar technique involves splitting an existing ring to form two

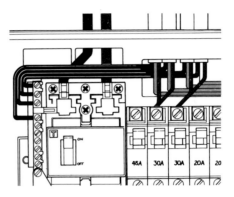

Above: *When you split an existing ring circuit to form two new rings, you need an additional 30-amp fuseway or MCB in the consumer unit. Wire up the cables as shown.*

Right: *The existing ring is split into two separate circuits, and the dotted section is discarded.*

radial circuits. This method is useful if you have sufficient socket outlets but you want a separate circuit to power an appliance such as an immersion heater without having to do any rewiring.

In this case you sever the ring at a convenient point to leave part of the circuit supplying sockets as a radial circuit; you must ensure that the floor area of the rooms it serves does not exceed 20sq m (215sq ft), and you

must replace the existing 30-amp fuse or MCB with a 20-amp one.

The other part of the circuit also becomes a 20-amp radial circuit, but now feeds the immersion heater or other fixed appliance not exceeding 4.8kW, instead of supplying sockets. Connect it to a spare fuseway fitted with a 20-amp fuse or MCB. You must blank off any socket outlets on this part of the original circuit; you can use one as a junction box to extend the circuit to the heater position, where it terminates in a 20-amp double-pole switch supplying the heater itself.

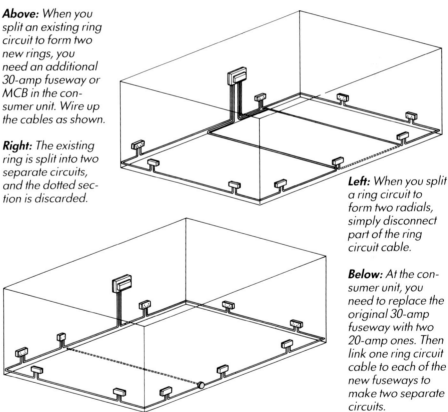

Left: *When you split a ring circuit to form two radials, simply disconnect part of the ring circuit cable.*

Below: *At the consumer unit, you need to replace the original 30-amp fuseway with two 20-amp ones. Then link one ring circuit cable to each of the new fuseways to make two separate circuits.*

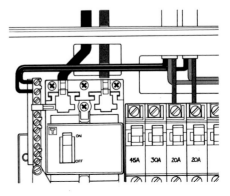

ADDING NEW RADIAL CIRCUITS

Yet another way of supplying extra socket outlets is to provide new radial sockets. This is a better option than a new ring circuit in some circumstances – for example, with an extension remote from the consumer unit where a ring would be wasteful of cable because of the long runs involved in wiring the ring out and back over such a distance.

You can wire up your radial circuit in one of two ways, and which you choose depends on the floor area of the rooms being served by the new circuit. Where this does not exceed 20sq m (215sq ft), you can use 2.5mm² cable, run from a 20-amp fuseway or MCB in the consumer unit or switchfuse unit supplying the circuit. If the floor area served exceeds 20sq m but is less than 50sq m (540sq ft), you must use 4.0mm² cable, and fit a 30-amp fuse or MCB to protect it. If a fuse is used rather than an MCB, it must be a cartridge type, not a rewirable fuse. There is no limit to the number of sockets or other outlets that each circuit can serve.

The circuit itself can supply sockets, or you can run spurs off it so long as their number does not exceed the number of sockets on the main circuit. Spurs can be wired from sockets or 30-amp junction boxes.

Start work on the circuit by installing mounting boxes for the various accessories it will serve. Cut chases for concealed wiring if needed, and run in the circuit cables. Make the connections at each outlet point, and finish by taking the cable back to the consumer unit or new switchfuse unit. Fit the correct fuse or MCB for the circuit, and link the live circuit cable core to it. Take the neutral core to the unit's neutral terminal, and the earth (protected by green/yellow PVC sleeving) to the earth terminal.

Options

Two ways of wiring the circuit:

• For a floor area not exceeding 20sq m (215sq ft), use 2.5mm² two-core-and-earth cable for the circuit wiring, and fit a 20-amp fuse or MCB at the consumer unit or switchfuse unit.

• For a floor area of between 20 and 50sq m (215 to 540sq ft), use 4.0mm² cable for the circuit wiring and fit a 30-amp fuse (cartridge type only) or MCB at the consumer unit or new switchfuse unit.

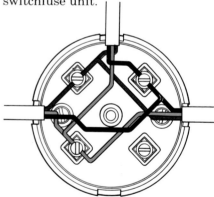

Above: Wire the new circuit cable cores to a spare 20-amp or 30-amp fuseway in the consumer unit.

Right: A new radial circuit can supply spurs fed from circuit sockets or junction boxes, and each spur can then feed a socket outlet or FCU.

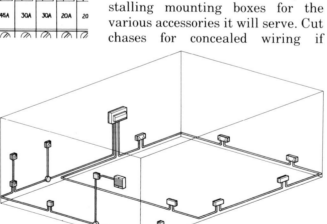

Above: You can connect spurs into the new radial circuit at any convenient point using a 30-amp junction box.

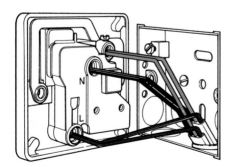

Above: Intermediate sockets on the new circuit are wired up as ring circuit sockets, with incoming and outgoing cables.

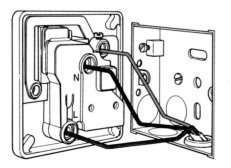

Above: The end socket on the circuit, and any sockets supplied as spurs, will have just one circuit cable present.

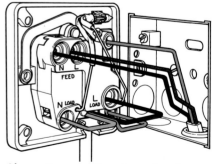

Above: You can also wire up fused connection units on spurs as shown to supply individual fixed appliances.

Wiring at the consumer unit

If you are using a spare fuseway at the consumer unit, make sure that you fit the fuse or MCB at the right place in the sequence; the highest-rated fuses should be nearest the main on/off switch. The same applies if you are adding a switchfuse unit to supply the extra circuit(s). The incoming circuit cable live core goes to the terminal on the fuseholder or MCB, the neutral core to the neutral terminal block and the earth to the earth terminal block.

Radial circuits for lighting

If you have a lot of individual plug-in table and standard lamps, you may find that they are using 13-amp socket outlets you would rather have free for other appliances. One way of overcoming this problem is to provide a separate radial socket outlet circuit just for the lights, so freeing the existing 13-amp sockets for other uses.

Wire up the circuit using 1.0mm² two-core-and-earth cable, as for ordinary lighting circuits, but in this case you run it to a series of 5-amp round-pin socket outlets. These can be switched or unswitched, though the former are preferable. You then fit each light with a matching 5-amp round-pin plug, ready for connection to the new circuit. By using these plugs and sockets, you prevent other appliances being plugged into the lighting circuit

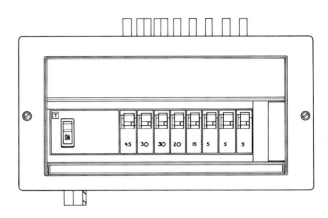

Right: Radial circuits can also supply a series of 5-amp round-pin socket outlets into which table and standard lamps can be plugged. Each circuit can supply a maximum of eight sockets, and is wired from a 5-amp fuseway in the consumer unit.

and overloading it. There is also no need to unplug the lights except for cleaning or bulb replacement.

Run the circuit just like an ordinary radial power circuit, with the cable running from socket to socket in series. However, spurs may not be added, and the circuit is restricted to a maximum of eight outlets to prevent overloading. Each outlet is rated as consuming 100 watts, even if bulbs of lower wattage are actually used in the lamps. At the consumer unit or switch-fuse unit, connect the circuit cable in the usual way (see above), and protect it with a

5-amp circuit fuse or MCB.

You can also provide this type of lighting circuit as a fused spur from an existing power circuit if this is more convenient. Instead of running the circuit cable back to a 5-amp fuseway in the consumer unit or switchfuse unit, you take it to a switched fused connection unit fitted with a 5-amp fuse. This is supplied as a spur, using 2.5mm² cable to link it to a convenient socket outlet or junction box. As with the separate circuit layout, the sockets should be wired in series, and a maximum of eight can be supplied from one FCU.

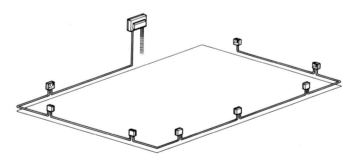

Left: The circuit is wired up as an in-line radial circuit, with the 1.0mm² cable running directly from one socket to the next. Spurs are not allowed on this type of circuit.

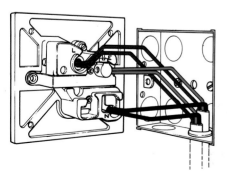

Above: The wiring for round-pin socket outlets is identical to that for 13-amp ones, with like cores linked to the same terminals.

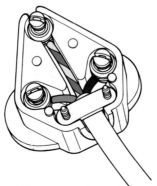

Above: Wire up round-pin plugs as shown here, and make sure that the flex sheathing is firmly anchored in the cord grip.

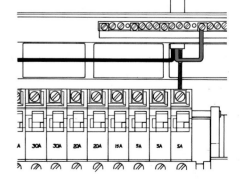

Above: Connect the live circuit cable core to a spare 5-amp fuseway or MCB, and link the neutral and earth to their terminals.

WIRING UP A COOKER UNIT

An electric cooker – or a split-level arrangement with separate components such as oven, hob and deep-fat fryer – is the biggest current consumer amongst electrical appliances, and must have its own circuit direct from the consumer unit. To allow you to isolate the cooker from the mains, the circuit cable is run either to a double-pole isolating switch (these are available with the word COOKER on the faceplate for ease of identification), or else to a combined switch and socket outlet known as a cooker control unit. The latter is currently being phased out in favour of double-pole switches, to eliminate the risk of flexes coming into contact with cooker hot-plates when appliances such as kettles and food processors are plugged into the control unit's socket outlet.

From the switch, run the cable to a position on the wall behind the cooker, oven or hob unit, where you install a special cooker connector unit. From here run cable (not flex, which cannot carry the high current required) to the cooker itself.

In theory a large cooker with oven, grill and four hotplates could consume as much as 50 amps, and to supply this would require a very large (and expensive) circuit cable. However, in practice you are unlikely to be using everything at once, or at their maximum heat settings. So to work out how big a cable you need to supply your cooker, you use a principle called diversity.

This assesses the first 10 amps of demand at 100 per cent, and the rest at 30 per cent. So for a cooker with a wattage of 11kW, the maximum current demand is just under 46 amps (11,000 watts divided by 240 volts). Applying the diversity formula, the circuit rating is 20.8 amps, calculated as follows:

100 per cent of 10 amps = 10
30 per cent of 36 amps = 10.8

If the cooker circuit is supplying a

Above: Cooker control units (left) are now being phased out. Use a 45-amp double-pole switch (top right) plus a connection unit (bottom right) instead.

socket in a cooker control unit, you add another 5 amps to the total.

Each commonly available size of cable has a current rating which depends on whether it is clipped to

Right: Run the circuit cable from the consumer unit to a 45-amp double-pole switch, then on to the cooker connection unit. Make the final connection to the cooker with cable, not flex. With split-level cookers, both components must be within 2 m (6 ft 6 in) of the switch.

the surface, embedded in plaster or enclosed in conduit, and on whether the circuit is protected by a rewirable fuse, a cartridge fuse or an MCB. For the example given above, you would need 2.5mm^2 cable if the circuit protection is a 30-amp cartridge fuse or MCB, and 4.0mm^2 cable if it is a 30-amp rewirable fuse.

If the calculated current demand falls between 27 and 36 amps, you should use 4.0mm^2 cable protected by a 45-amp cartridge fuse or MCB, and 6.0mm^2 cable with a 45-amp rewirable fuse. For demand between 36 and 48 amps, use 6.0mm^2 cable protected by a cartridge fuse or MCB, and 10.0mm^2 cable with a rewirable fuse. Again, the fuse or MCB should be rated at 45 amps.

Use cable of the same rating as the main circuit for the link between cooker and connector unit. Leave plenty of slack with free-standing cookers.

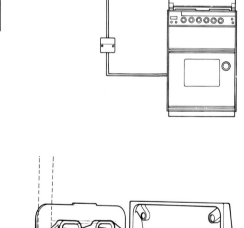

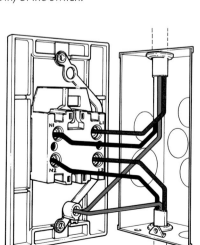

Above: Make the connections within a double-pole cooker switch as shown.

Above: Make the final link from the cooker to the connection unit with cable.

WIRING AN IMMERSION HEATER

In theory, a typical 3kW immersion heater could be connected to a 30-amp ring or radial circuit, but this would take the entire current-carrying capacity of the circuit. So in practice the heater is given its own independent radial circuit, run from its own fuseway or MCB in the consumer unit.

Run the standard circuit in 2.5mm² cable and protect it with a 20-amp fuse or MCB. You then run the circuit cable and connect it to a 20-amp double-pole switch situated close to the immersion heater. This switch allows the heater to be isolated for repairs or replacement if necessary. You can buy special switches marked WATER HEATER with a neon indicator and round flex entry hole on the front. If you intend to fit a dual-element heater or two separate elements, you need a special 20-amp changeover switch instead. This allows you to switch on one element or the other, depending on whether you want to heat just the water at the top of the cylinder or its entire contents.

From the double-pole switch, run 1.25mm² three-core heat-resisting flex to the heater itself, and connect it to the terminals on top of the heating element. If you are installing a dual-element or twin element, run two separate flexes – one to each of the two heaters – from the changeover switch.

This set-up provides manual switching only, and it is a good idea to incorporate an automatic timer control so that the heater provides hot water to coincide with periods of maximum demand and is not switched on unnecessarily at other times of the day. Special immersion heater timers are available, which you wire into the circuit between the 20-amp double-pole switch and the heater, using 2.5mm² cable between the switch and timer and 1.25mm² flex to link the timer and heater.

You can also provide remote switching for your immersion heater

Above: An immersion heater timer allows you to programme your heating periods and avoid unnecessary use of electricity.

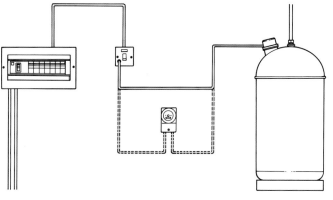

Left: Wire an immersion heater on its own circuit from the consumer unit, and take the cable to a 20-amp DP switch. Then run it on to a timer if one is fitted, and complete the circuit to the heater with a length of heat-resisting flex.

if you wish, providing a second switch in a convenient location such as the kitchen. For this you need two two-way double-pole switches, connected by three-core-and-earth cable rather like two-way switching but using 2.5mm² cable for the connection.

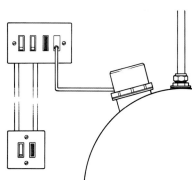

Right: A two-way switching arrangement allows control of the heater from a location downstairs as well as upstairs.

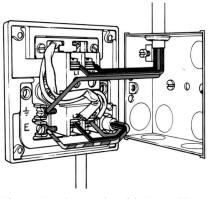

Above: Run the supply cable into a 20-amp double-pole switch, and link this to the heater with special heat-resisting flex.

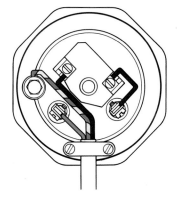

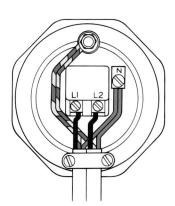

Left: With a single-element heater, connect the incoming flex cores as shown.

Right: With a dual-element heater, two flexes are needed. Link the live cores to the heaters, and take the neutrals and earths to the marked terminals.

WIRING AN ELECTRIC SHOWER

An instantaneous electric shower is also a big consumer of current – the latest models are rated at up to 8.4kW – so, like a cooker, it must be given its own independent circuit from the consumer unit. If you are planning to install one, it is worth checking with your electricity board to see whether your main service fuse needs upgrading to cope with the extra current demand.

The circuit cable to the shower runs from a fuseway or MCB in the consumer unit to a double-pole switch near the shower, and then runs directly to the shower heater itself, where it is wired directly into a terminal block. The double-pole switch must be a ceiling-mounted cord-operated type if it is located within 2m (6 ft 6 in) of the bath or shower; otherwise a wall-mounted type can be fitted. Both should have a neon indicator to show whether the power to the shower is on.

For showers rated at up to 7kW, consuming just under 30 amps, you need a 30-amp circuit fuse or MCB. If the fuse is the rewirable type, you must run the circuit in 6.0mm² cable; with a cartridge fuse or MCB, you can use 4.0mm² cable instead. For more powerful showers, use 6.0mm² cable and a 45-amp fuse, plus a higher-rated 45-amp double-pole switch.

To install the wiring, work back-

wards from the shower unit. The cable between switch and shower will have to run down the wall of the shower cubicle. It can be surface-mounted, but it is better to run it in a chase behind the cubicle tiling so it emerges directly behind the shower heater and is completely concealed from view. Seal the point where the cable emerges from the wall with silicone mastic, so that water cannot penetrate behind the tiles and cause premature failure of the plaster or the tile adhesive.

If your are installing a ceiling-

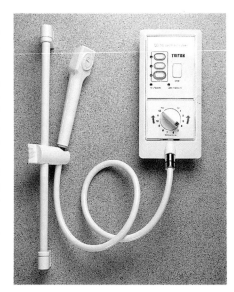

Right: Modern instantaneous showers are neat, compact self-contained units.

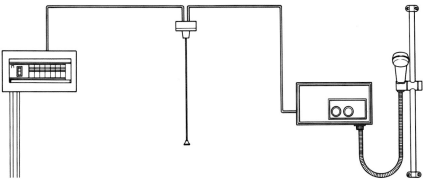

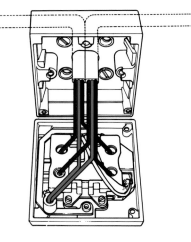

Above: Run the circuit cable to a ceiling-mounted double-pole switch, then to the shower.

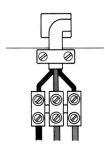

Right: Connect the cable cores to the terminals within the shower casing.

mounted switch, make sure that its baseplate is secured either to a joist or to a batten fitted between adjacent joists.

Remember to cross-bond the shower supply pipe to earth – see page 37 – before using the shower.

Left: Make the connections within the ceiling-mounted cord-operated double-pole switch as shown here. Make sure that the switch baseplate is securely mounted.

Right: Provide power to a small single-point water heater via a spur to a fused connection unit fitted with a 13-amp fuse.

Single-point heaters

Small single-point water heaters are often used in cloakrooms to provide a hot water supply for a washbasin, and if they are rated at below 3kW they can take their power supply from an FCU wired as a spur from a nearby power circuit, or an FCU on the main circuit itself.

Wire up the spur using 2.5mm² cable, and fit a 13-amp fuse in the connection unit fuseholder. You can now either run cable direct from the fused connection unit to the heater terminals, or link the two with a length of 1.25mm² three-core heat-resisting flex.

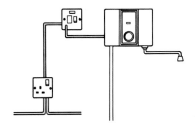

WIRING STORAGE HEATERS

Storage heaters contain heat storage materials which are heated up by an enclosed element, and are run on cheap night-rate electricity supplied from a separate timer-controlled switchfuse unit or consumer unit. A dual-rate meter records the night-time electricity consumption of the heaters as they are charged up, and they then discharge their stored heat gradually during the day. Storage heaters are available with heat output ratings ranging from about 1.7kW up to 3.5kW.

Older-style storage heaters, now no longer available, also contained a fan which was used to circulate air through the heater.

Each heater will require its own radial circuit (except for the lowest-rated models, where two may be run from the same circuit). Run the circuit from a 20-amp fuseway or MCB in the consumer unit to a

Right: Modern night storage heaters are much less obtrusive and considerably more efficient than earlier types. They are available in a wide range of styles and heat outputs.

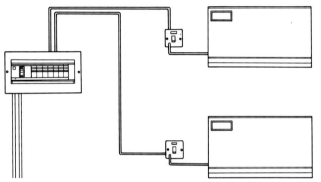

Left: Individual heaters have their own circuits, run from their own timer-controlled consumer unit to a 20-amp double-pole switch next to the heater. The switch is connected to the heater with heavy-duty three-core flex.

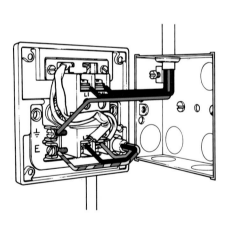

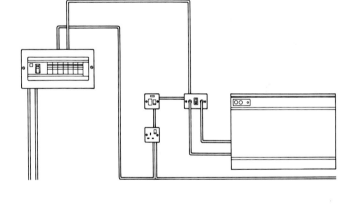

Right: Old-style fan-assisted storage heaters had a separate power supply for the fan, available 24 hours a day via a spur run to a fused connection unit. The heater and fan were wired to a special dual switch as shown.
Left: The wiring within the 20-amp double-pole switch.

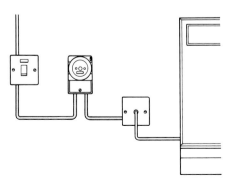

Above: If you want to put individual heaters under timer control, wire the timer in after the double-pole switch and then run cable in to a flex outlet plate.

20-amp double-pole switch with a neon indicator and flex outlet. Mount this next to the heater position, and connect the heater to it using three-core flex of the appropriate size: you need 1.25mm² flex for heaters rated at up to 3kW, and 1.5mm² flex for those rated at up to 3.5kW. The flex should be the heat-resistant type. Where individual time clocks are used to control the heaters, the clock is wired into the heater circuit between the DP switch and a flex outlet plate.

The now-obsolete older-style fan-

assisted heaters were controlled from a special 25-amp dual switch wired up as shown in the diagram above. Power for the heater was taken to one side of the switch as before, via a radial circuit from the consumer unit. Since the fan needed to operate during the day when the heater circuit was off, it needed an unrestricted 24-hour-a-day power supply. This was provided via a fused spur taken from a nearby power circuit and on to the fan side of the switch. Separate flexes ran to the fan and heater.

INSTALLING A NEW CONSUMER UNIT

Modern consumer units are attractive one-piece housings containing all the circuit connections and protective devices needed for an up-to-date wiring system. If your existing unit is an old-fashioned one fitted with rewirable fuses, it is a good idea to replace it with a new unit containing MCBs and an RCD.

When buying a new unit, select one that contains an RCD as well, to provide protection for the system against earth current leakages and protection for you and your family against electric shock. Work out carefully how many circuits you need or are likely to want in the future; each circuit MCB will occupy one module in the unit, and an RCD generally needs four modules, so you may need a 12-way or even a 16-way unit to cope with the demands of power and lighting circuits, circuits to cookers, immersion heaters and showers, plus perhaps circuits to outbuildings.

The new consumer unit should be fitted within 2m of the meter position, and must be on a fire-resistant board or surface. In practice you are likely to want to site it where the old fusebox was, so your first step is to have the meter tails disconnected by the electricity board. Ask them to provide a temporary power supply to a socket outlet so you have power and light.

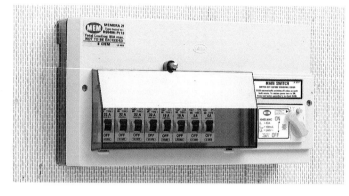

Before you disconnect any cables, label the cable sheaths so you can identify each one later. Carefully disconnect the cores of each cable in turn from their terminals, and draw the cable out of the old unit. When you have disconnected everything, unscrew and remove the old unit and set it aside. Mount the new unit, and fit your chosen array of MCBs plus the RCD on the busbar within the unit. Remember that the MCBs with the highest current ratings should be fitted nearest the RCD. Now reconnect the circuit live cores to their MCBs, and take all the neutral and earth cores to their respective terminal blocks. Double-check all the connections and arrange the cables neatly. You should then label each circuit clearly so you know which MCB controls which circuit, and call the electricity board to reconnect the mains supply.

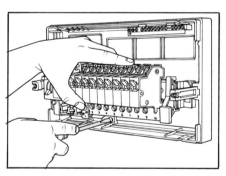

1 Mount the baseplate of the new unit on its backing board and fit the MCBs to the live busbar.

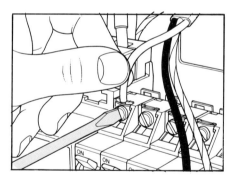

2 Run in the individual circuit cables, strip the cores and connect each live core to the terminal on its MCB.

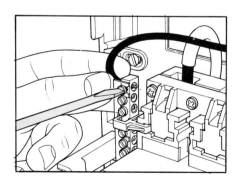

3 Connect all the neutral cores to the neutral terminal block at one side of the unit. Leave plenty of slack.

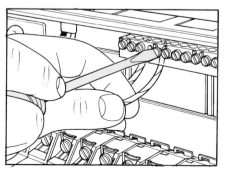

4 Complete the connection by linking all the earth cores to the main earthing terminal after fitting sleeving to them.

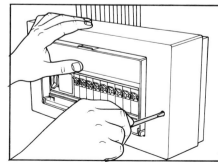

5 Call in the electricity board or a qualified electrician to connect the meter tails, then fit its cover.

WORKING OUT OF DOORS

WORKING OUT OF DOORS

Electricity can be just as valuable outside the home as within it – for example, to provide outdoor lighting, drive power tools for use in the garden, or supply light and heat in a greenhouse or workshop. However, the great outdoors is a hostile and potentially dangerous environment as far as electricity is concerned, so great care must be taken to protect outdoor circuits from the effects of the weather and from accidental damage. Perhaps even more importantly, steps must also be taken to prevent anyone using electricity out of doors receiving a potentially fatal electric shock.

The present wiring regulations have recognized the importance of this last point, and now require that any socket or sockets providing power to tools or appliances that will be used out of doors must be protected by a high-sensitivity residual current device (RCD) – on the circuit itself, within the socket concerned or within a special plug or adaptor connected to the appliance.

RUNNING CABLE OVERHEAD

If you want to run a power supply to an outbuilding such as a garage, greenhouse or workshop, one way of doing so is to install an overhead power line between the two buildings. This must be run as an independent sub-circuit from its own fuseway in the main consumer unit in the home, or from a separate switchfuse unit next to the consumer unit if there are no spare fuseways. The circuit should be protected by a 30-amp fuse. Ordinary PVC-sheathed cable can be used throughout.

Take the cable through a hole in the house wall and on to the outbuilding. There are several rules governing how this run must be installed. Firstly, the cable must be a minimum of 3.5m (11 ft 6 in) above ground level throughout the run, and this must be increased to a height of 5.2m (17 ft) if the cable passes over a driveway. This means you will probably need a post on the outbuilding to carry that end of the cable, and intermediate posts may also be needed. These should be placed at maximum 5m (16 ft 6 in) intervals along the cable run.

Where the span of cable between supports is less than 3.5m (11 ft 6 in), no additional support for the cable is needed; you can simply secure it to the supports at either end with cable clips. For spans greater than 3.5m, you must use a supporting wire called a catenary – a length of stout galvanized wire

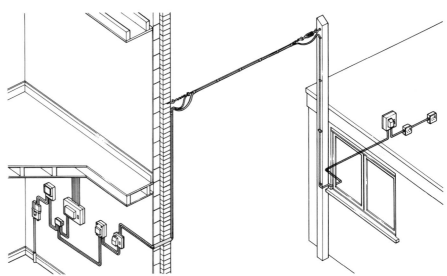

Above: An overhead circuit to an outbuilding starts at a spare fuseway or switchfuse unit in the house and runs via an RCD to another switchfuse unit in the outbuilding.

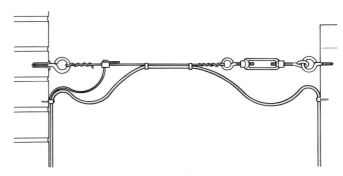

Right: For spans over 3.5m (11 ft 6 in) long, the cable must be supported on a properly tensioned catenary wire which is itself cross-bonded to earth for complete safety. Drip loops stop water getting into either building.

stretched between screw eyes. You then sling the cable beneath it using special ties, with drip loops at each end of the suspended sections to allow water to run off without entering the buildings. The wire must be earthed for safety reasons.

Note that you may attach a cable run above ground to solid structures such as garden walls, but you must not run it along fences because of the risk of damage to the cable if the fence blows down.

At the outbuilding end of the circuit, take the cable into the building and connect it to a small switchfuse unit, again containing a 30-amp fuse. This allows you to isolate the sub-circuit within the building, as well as from the consumer unit position within the house. From there, you can run individual light and power circuits as required – see page 89.

RUNNING CABLE UNDERGROUND

Running outdoor power lines overhead is at best unsightly, and there is always the risk of accidental damage caused by, for example, careless handling of ladders. The alternative is to bury the cable run underground, out of harm's way.

One way of doing this is to run the buried section of cable in PVC-sheathed cable within impact-resistant PVC conduit, buried at least 450mm (18 in) below ground level. This has the advantage that the same cable can be used for the whole run. The alternative is to use armoured or mineral-insulated copper-clad (MICC) cable, both of which can be laid directly in the trench.

Armoured cable has a tough outer sheathing concealing a layer of flexible metal mesh armour which does double duty as the cable's earth core. Where the cable enters the home or outbuilding, use a special junction box to connect the cable to ordinary PVC-sheathed cable for the indoor sections of the run. You need to fit the ends of the armoured cable with special screwed compression glands which connect the cable to the box and provide the necessary earth continuity for the circuit.

MICC cable is much thinner than armoured cable – for example, it will pass easily through the openings in

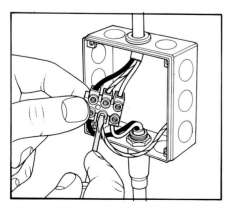
Above: With armoured cable, you need a special screwed gland to connect it to PVC-sheathed cable in a junction box.

Right: Underground circuits are less prone to accidental damage than an overhead supply. PVC-sheathed cable must be protected by impact-resistant conduit, but armoured or mineral-insulated cable can be buried directly in the ground.

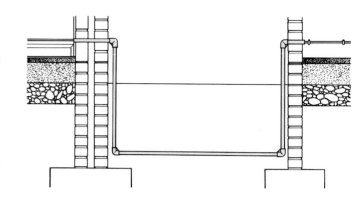

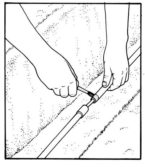

1 Mark out the line of the trench, and dig it out to a depth of 450mm (18in).

2 Lay lengths of PVC conduit on a bed of sand along the base of the trench.

3 Feed in the circuit cable from one end of the conduit run to the other.

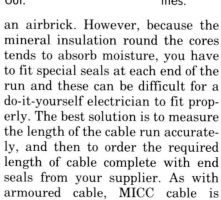

4 Solvent-weld all the joints together carefully to keep ground water out.

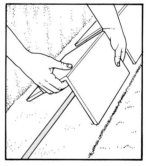

5 Provide additional protection by covering the conduit with ridge tiles.

6 Back-fill the trench, packing the subsoil down to prevent subsidence.

an airbrick. However, because the mineral insulation round the cores tends to absorb moisture, you have to fit special seals at each end of the run and these can be difficult for a do-it-yourself electrician to fit properly. The best solution is to measure the length of the cable run accurately, and then to order the required length of cable complete with end seals from your supplier. As with armoured cable, MICC cable is

generally two-core, with the copper sheathing acting as the earth continuity conductor, so you need special screwed compression glands as above to connect the cable to the junction box at each end of the run.

If you use PVC-sheathed cable in conduit, you will need 90-degree elbows and couplers to join the lengths of conduit, and you must solvent-weld all joints as the run is made up to ensure it is watertight.

CIRCUITS
IN OUTBUILDINGS

Within the outbuilding itself, the incoming circuit cable runs direct to a small switchfuse unit (unless you have used armoured or MICC cable for the outdoor section, in which case this terminates at a metal junction box, and PVC-sheathed cable runs from that to the switchfuse unit). Since you are probably planning to use the sockets in the outbuilding to drive power tools and equipment out of doors, you must give them RCD protection. The best way of doing this is to include a high-sensitivity RCD within the switchfuse unit. This will also serve as the main isolating switch for the outbuilding.

The circuits within the outbuilding can be arranged in one of two ways. The first method is to fit a 20- or 30-amp fuse or MCB within the switchfuse unit, and then to wire up sockets and fused connection units within the building as a standard radial circuit using 2.5mm² cable. Fit one fused connection unit with a

5-amp fuse, and run a spur in 1.0mm² cable to supply the light fittings. Such a spur can feed up to eight lights, so should meet all reasonable requirements. Use a switched FCU to act as the on/off switch for the lights, or give each fitting its own independent switch.

The second alternative is to provide separate circuits within the switchfuse unit for power and lighting, in which case you will need two separate fuseways. Fit one with a 20-amp fuse or MCB, and wire up

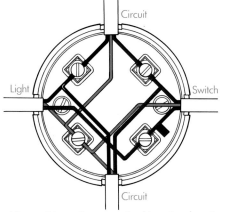

Above: *Use a four-terminal junction box to provide independent light switching.*

the socket circuit as a standard radial circuit. Fit the other fuseway with a 5-amp fuse and run a standard loop-in or junction-box lighting circuit from it.

You can use ordinary plastic wiring accessories and surface-mounted boxes within the outbuilding, but it is better to choose tougher metal-clad accessories and metal boxes to guard against the risk of damage. If you use metal-clad accessories, remember to fit a short length of sleeved earth wire between the earth terminal on the accessory face-plate and the earth terminal within the metal mounting box.

The wiring within the outbuilding can simply be clipped to wall and ceiling surfaces, but if you want a neater installation, enclose it in mini-trunking instead.

In wooden sheds, mount sockets on battens which have been secured to the shed walls by screws driven through from outside. In greenhouses, bolt the battens to the greenhouse framework. If the outbuilding has pressed concrete walls, use special panel fixings.

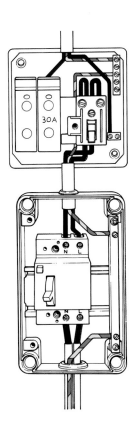

Left: *The circuit to the outbuilding is wired from a spare 30-amp fuseway in the consumer unit, or from a separate switchfuse unit if no spare fuseway is available. The cable then runs to an RCD and on to the outbuilding.*

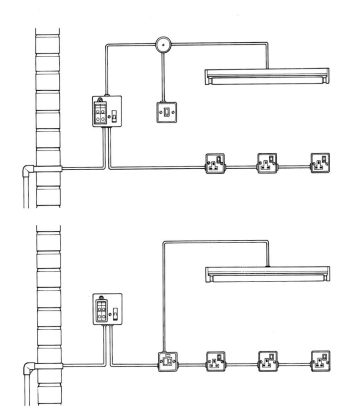

Right: *Within the outbuilding, the circuit cable runs to a second switchfuse unit. Either provide separate circuits for light and power (top), or run the lights via a fused spur (bottom).*

INSTALLING
OUTDOOR LIGHTING

If you want to install light fittings along your drive or in the garden, you cannot run them as a spur from an indoor circuit. Instead, they must be supplied by their own independent circuit run from a 5-amp fuseway in the consumer unit, or in a new switchfuse unit fitted alongside it. For safety's sake, it is a good idea to protect the circuit with its own RCD unless the whole home is already protected in this way.

The first step in planning an outdoor lighting circuit is to decide on the positions of the light fittings themselves. You can then plan how best to run the cable between them; it will generally run from the house to the first light, and then loop on to the next in series.

You also need to think about switching arrangements for the lights. A single light or a set of lights in one location will probably be switched from one position inside the house, but if you have lighting for different purposes – lighting the drive and the garden pond, for example – you will want each set of lights switched independently. You may also want to provide outdoor switch control, perhaps linked to a time switch, a photocell or a passive infra-red detector.

You will obviously have to run the circuit cable underground, and the best solution is to use PVC-sheathed cable run in impact-resistant PVC conduit, as for an underground power supply to an outbuilding. If the light fittings have integral terminal blocks, you can run the cable directly into each light and out again to the next one in the series. If there is a flex tail leading to the light, you will have to fit a conduit box close to the light to contain the connections between cable and flex, which will be made as usual with connector blocks.

Make sure that all fittings are designed for outdoor use, and that you have mounted them securely.

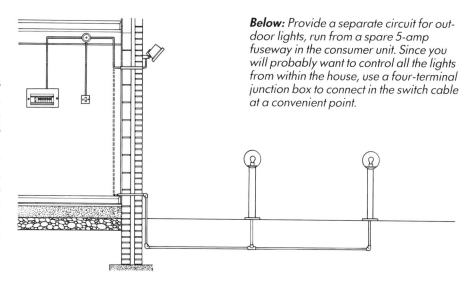

Below: Provide a separate circuit for outdoor lights, run from a spare 5-amp fuseway in the consumer unit. Since you will probably want to control all the lights from within the house, use a four-terminal junction box to connect in the switch cable at a convenient point.

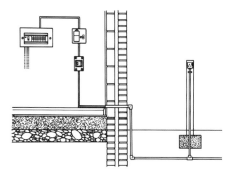

Right: Connect the cores of the circuit cable directly to the fitting's terminals.
Below: For flexibility, wire up a 30-amp radial circuit feeding a number of outdoor socket outlets and use plug-in lights.

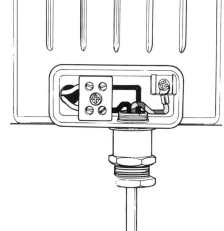

Always use waterproof cable entries to ensure that no water gets into the light fittings themselves.

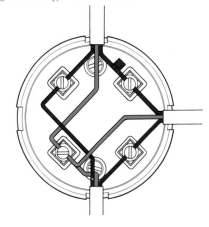

Above: Use a four-terminal junction box to connect in the cables to the switch and to the lights themselves.

Above: Globe fittings provide an attractively diffused light, and different versions can be wall-mounted or set on posts.

Left: Low-voltage light fittings are quick and easy to install – the cable can simply be laid on top of the soil surface – and are completely safe to use. A range of different styles is available, some on spikes for ground-level mounting and others suitable for attachment to walls, piers or posts.

Wire it in 2.5mm² PVC-sheathed cable run through impact-resistant PVC conduit buried in a 450mm (18in) deep trench in the ground. Then at each socket position, run the conduit up the mounting post to the socket and use waterproof cable entries to ensure the installation remains absolutely watertight in all kinds of adverse weather.

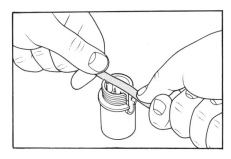

1 Most low-voltage lights have special spike connectors. Decide where you want the light on the cable run, press the cable in and fit the cap.

Low-voltage lighting

An alternative to using mains-voltage lighting out of doors is to opt for a low-voltage installation instead. The individual light fittings are linked in series by special low-voltage cable which need not be buried in the ground; it can simply be left lying on the surface, or can be clipped to walls, fences, trees and so on. The power is supplied by a small transformer located in the home, in an outbuilding or in a weatherproof enclosure built at a convenient point in the garden, and is itself connected to a convenient mains supply.

Various types of outdoor low-voltage light fittings are available, usually taking 6-volt car light bulbs. Some are designed to be mounted on a spike driven into the ground, while others can be attached to walls, piers or posts. The low-voltage cable is usually connected to terminals within the light, or simply passes through a special clamping block containing two pin contacts which pierce the cable's outer sheathing to make the electrical connections.

With most low-voltage lighting arrangements, there is a limit to the number of lights the transformer can power; check before you buy.

Outdoor socket circuits

You can also power outdoor light fittings from a network of socket outlets sited at strategic points around the garden. These should be the weatherproof type, which accept a special plug to guarantee a water-proof connection, although you can use ordinary three-pin plugs with shower-proof sockets incorporating an RCD (see below).

The advantage of using a socket circuit like this is that you can move lights around easily to achieve different lighting effects at different times of the year, especially if you use fittings on spikes for easy location.

The socket circuit must be an independent circuit run from a 30-amp fuse or MCB in the consumer unit, and the circuit must be protected by a high sensitivity RCD.

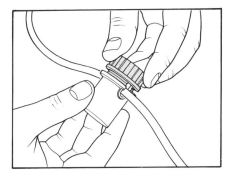

2 Screw on the weatherproof cap to force the cable down onto the spikes and make the connection. Then fit the lamp.

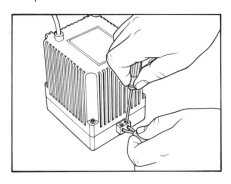

3 Run the low-voltage cable back to the transformer and connect it to its terminals. Site the transformer under cover and plug it in.

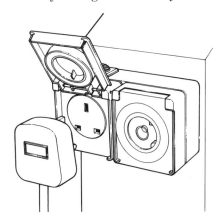

Above: Outdoor socket outlets must have RCD protection. If you want just one socket, buy one with its own integral RCD.

PLANNING A REWIRE

The ultimate challenge to the do-it-yourself electrician is to rewire a home completely – a task that can sound daunting. However, the only difference between rewiring and smaller electrical projects is one of scale; you do not need any additional skills to enable you to carry out the job, and you stand to save a lot of money by doing everything yourself instead of calling in a contractor.

However, you must be prepared for considerable upheaval around the home as floorboards are lifted and walls chased out, and only careful planning will minimize this. The secret of success is to divide the job into manageable zones, concentrating on one circuit at a time so that at the end of each day you can restore power to the parts you have been working on.

Begin by planning your requirements one floor at a time, working with a rough plan of the house. What you are aiming to do is to record the approximate position of every new light, socket outlet and wiring accessory you intend to install. This is an invaluable aid when estimating materials and working out overall costs. Here are some points to bear in mind as you do this.

Upstairs

Bedrooms In bedrooms the main requirement is for socket outlets in convenient positions such as beside the bed and by the dressing table. You may want to fit new wall lights and incorporate two-way switching, or add a shaver socket.

Bathrooms Good lighting is essential here, especially for shaving and applying makeup. You could fit ex-tra lights, or a combined shaver and striplight unit. You may want power for an electric shower, with its own circuit, or to make provision for a heated towel rail or a wall heater.

Landings Again, look for improved lighting plus two-way switching, and provide a socket outlet for the vacuum cleaner.

Loft Don't forget to add a light in the loft, switched on the landing for convenience.

Below: *To plan your wiring needs, start by drawing upstairs and downstairs floor plans of your house; they need not be completely accurate or to scale. Then mark in the positions of fixtures and fitted furniture so you can decide exactly where you want light fittings, switches, socket outlets, fused connection units and other outlets such as TV and phone sockets.*

Downstairs

Living rooms Make sure there are enough sockets, and improve lighting and switching arrangements. Add TV aerial and phone sockets.

Kitchens In kitchens, extra sockets are again top priority, plus FCUs for fixed appliances. Remember a circuit for the cooker.

Halls Centralize lighting controls here and add a socket outlet and phone point if you like.

KEY
○ Light position
⌷ Switch position
⊡ Socket outlet
■ Fused connection unit (FCU)
□ Double pole switch (DP)
P Phone
T TV aerial
S Shaver socket

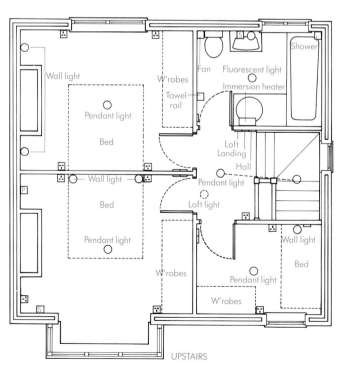

UPSTAIRS

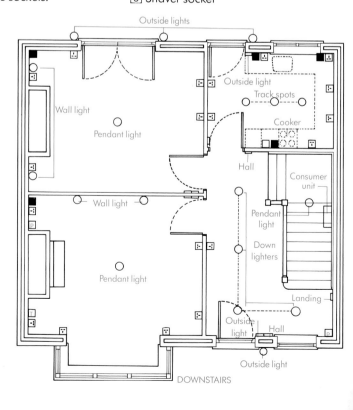

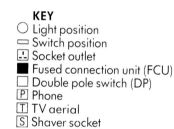

DOWNSTAIRS

ESTIMATING MATERIALS

Accessories

Use your floor plans – see opposite – to produce a detailed list of all the different wiring accessories and mounting boxes you will need for the job. Take a look at the various styles of wiring accessory now available. Apart from the ubiquitous white plastic, there are several ranges in ornate brass or satin chrome, or with coloured faceplates. You may decide to have different finishes in different rooms.

You can then present your list of requirements to several potential suppliers and ask them to quote prices. You should be able to negotiate a sizeable discount, especially on items you need in quantity such as socket outlets.

Cable and flex

Cable is expensive, and you are likely to need a lot of it, so you do not want to buy more than you require. However, it is virtually impossible at this stage to estimate quantities accurately except for special cases such as cooker circuits where you can measure the length of the cable run fairly accurately. The best solution is to buy complete drums containing 50 or 100m (164 or 328 ft) of the cables you will use most – 1.0mm² for lighting circuits, and 2.5mm² for power circuits – and to buy other heavy-duty cables by the metre as and when you need them.

You will also need small quantities of flex of various ratings; again buy these by the metre.

Sundries

Make a separate list of all the wiring sundries you are likely to need during the course of the installation; there is nothing more irritating than being held up because you have forgotten some small but vital component. The list includes items such as green/yellow sleeving for bare earth cores, rubber grommets for flush metal mounting boxes, conduit and mini-trunking, insulating tape, cable clips, connector blocks and fuses.

Finally, make sure that you have all the specialist and general-purpose tools you will need for the job. It may be worth hiring specialist tools such as chasing machines for the duration of the work.

WIRING ACCESSORIES

Power circuits
- Single socket outlets ☐
- Double socket outlets ☐
- Triple socket outlets ☐
- RCD socket outlets ☐
- Metalclad socket outlets ☐
- 5-amp round-hole socket outlets ☐
- Weatherproof outdoor sockets ☐
- Unswitched fused connection units ☐
- Switched fused connection units ☐
- Switched FCUs with flex outlet ☐
- Flex outlet plates ☐
- 20-amp double-pole switches ☐
- 20-amp DP switches with flex outlet ☐
- 20-amp dual immersion heater switch ☐
- Immersion heater timer ☐
- 30-amp DP switches ☐
- 45-amp DP switches ☐
- Switch mounting boxes ☐
- Cord-operated DP ceiling switches ☐
- Cooker control unit ☐
- Cooker unit mounting box ☐
- Cooker connector unit ☐
- Shaver supply unit ☐
- Shaver unit mounting box ☐
- Shaver socket outlet ☐
- Single flush mounting boxes ☐
- Single surface mounting boxes ☐
- Double flush mounting boxes ☐
- Double surface mounting boxes ☐
- 30-amp junction boxes ☐
- 13-amp plugs ☐
- 5-amp plugs ☐

Lighting circuits
- One-gang one-way plateswitches ☐
- One-gang two-way plateswitches ☐
- Two-gang two-way plateswitches ☐
- Multi-gang plateswitches ☐
- Architrave plateswitches ☐
- Cord-operated ceiling switches ☐
- One-gang dimmer switches ☐
- Two-gang dimmer switches ☐
- Metalclad plateswitches ☐
- Weatherproof outdoor switches ☐
- Flush mounting boxes ☐
- Surface mounting boxes ☐
- Ceiling roses ☐
- Pendant lampholders ☐
- Battenholders ☐
- Luminaire support couplers ☐
- Conduit (BESA) boxes ☐
- Three-terminal junction boxes ☐
- Four-terminal junction boxes ☐

Other circuits
- Telephone socket outlets ☐
- TV/FM socket outlets ☐
- Mounting boxes ☐
- Door bell and push ☐
- Central heating controls ☐

Consumer unit
- Consumer unit (? ways) ☐
- 5/6-amp MCBs ☐
- 15/16-amp MCBs ☐
- 20-amp MCBs ☐
- 30/32-amp MCBs ☐
- 40/45-amp MCBs ☐
- Integral RCD ☐

Cable and flex
- 1.0mm² two-core-and-earth cable ☐
- 1.0mm² three-core-and-earth cable ☐
- 2.5mm² two-core-and-earth cable ☐
- 4.0mm² two-core-and-earth cable ☐
- 6.0mm² two-core-and-earth cable ☐
- 10.0mm² two-core-and-earth cable ☐
- 0.5mm² two-core-and-earth flex ☐
- 0.5mm² two-core flex ☐
- 0.75mm² two-core-and-earth flex ☐
- 1.0mm² two-core-and-earth flex ☐
- 1.25mm² two-core-and-earth flex ☐
- 1.5mm² two-core-and-earth flex ☐
- Heat-resisting flex ☐
- Single-core meter tails ☐
- Single core earth cable for cross-bonding ☐
- Earth clamps ☐
- Coaxial aerial cable ☐
- Telephone cable ☐
- Bell wire ☐
- Multi-core flex for heating controls ☐

Sundries
- PVC conduit and fittings ☐
- Mini-trunking and fittings ☐
- Cable clips ☐
- 5- and 30-amp connector blocks ☐
- PVC insulating tape ☐
- Green/yellow PVC sleeving ☐
- Rubber grommets for knockouts ☐
- Plug fuses ☐

WORK SEQUENCE

Stage 1

The easiest place to start rewiring is in the loft, where you can tackle all the upstairs lighting circuits in comparative comfort. You may be able to use existing conduit to run new cables down to existing switch positions. As you work, label the sheathing at each end of every cable run to indicate what it does and where it goes. This will be invaluable both to you and any future occupant tackling repair work.

Stage 2

Next, tackle the wiring in the void between the ground and first floors. Here you will be running cables for upstairs power circuits, circuits for appliances such as showers in bathrooms, and the circuits for most of the downstairs lights.

To minimize disruption, run in all the cables first, working in one room at a time so the whole house does not become a forest of lifted floorboards. Draw cables up to the positions of new accessories, leaving generous amounts so that connections will be easy to make. Cut chases and install light fittings as required.

When you replace the floorboards, mark on them the positions of cable routes underneath for future reference, and cut boards so you have only a short section to lift above vital connection points such as junction boxes and ceiling roses.

Stage 3

The final stage is to carry out the rewiring at ground-floor level — chiefly circuits to socket outlets, and specialist ones to appliances such as cookers. The next step is to complete two-way switching on the stairs. You then run all the main circuit cables down to the consumer unit position, mount your new consumer unit and connect in all the cables.

You can now finish removing all old cables, and arrange for the supply to be switched over from your old fuseboxes to the new system.

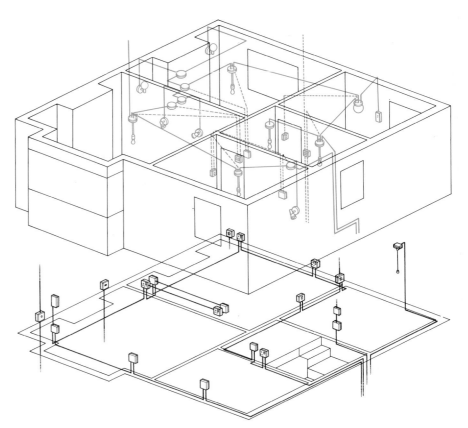

Tackle the wiring in the loft first, then do the upstairs power circuits and downstairs light circuits at bedroom floor level. Finish off by wiring the downstairs power circuits.

GLOSSARY OF TERMS

In this book, you may come across various terms which are unfamiliar. Here are some of the most common.

Amp
The unit of electric current, often abbreviated to A. Divide an appliance's wattage by the mains voltage (240) to work out how much current it uses.

Architrave switch
A narrow light switch, designed for mounting on door architraves or in places where space is limited.

Battenholder
A utility light fitting for wall or ceiling mounting, consisting of a straight or angled lampholder and fixed baseplate.

Cable
One or more metallic insulated conductors (or cores) covered with a protective insulating outer sheath, used for wiring up individual circuits on a house wiring system.

Cartridge fuse
A fuse consisting of fuse wire within a tubular holder, fitted in some older-style fuseboxes and in modern plugs and fused connection units.

Circuits
Complete paths round which current flows – along the live conductor to where it is needed, then back to its source along the neutral conductor.

Conduit
Round or oval PVC tube, used to protect cable runs beneath plaster, out of doors or underground.

Conduit box
Round mounting box, also called a BESA box, used to contain the electrical connections to wall and ceiling light fittings.

Consumer unit
The main control box that governs the supply of electricity to all circuits in the house. The unit contains the system's main on/off switch, and fuses or circuit breakers protecting each individual circuit in the house. Often called a fusebox.

Core
The 'trade' term for the conductors within flex and cable.

Cross-bonding
The linking of exposed metalwork – water pipes, sinks, baths, towel rails and so on – to earth for electrical safety purposes.

Double-pole switch
On/off switch that cuts both the live and neutral sides of the circuit, so completely isolating the appliance it controls from the mains supply when switched off.

Earthing
The provision of a continuous conductor on circuits to protect the user from certain electrical faults. Earth conductors are insulated with green/yellow striped PVC in flex, and are covered with slip-on green/yellow sleeving where they are exposed in cables.

Earth leakage circuit breaker
Former name for protective device now properly referred to as a residual current device (RCD).

Flex
Short for flexible cord, and consisting of insulated conductors within a flexible outer sheath and used to link appliances and pendant lights to the mains.

Fusebox
Old-style control unit containing the system's main on/off switch and the fuses protecting individual circuits in the house. Now widely replaced by modern consumer units.

Fused connection unit (FCU)
Wiring accessory allowing an appliance to be permanently connected to the mains, instead of being plugged in at a socket outlet.

Fused spur
A branch line off a main power circuit, protected by a fuse of lower rating than the main circuit fuse.

Fuses
Protective devices inserted into electrical circuits and plugs to prevent overloading.

Gangs
A term that describes the number of individual switches or socket outlets contained in one wiring accessory.

Grommets
Small plastic washers used in metal mounting boxes to stop the cable chafing on the edges of a knockout.

IEE Wiring Regulations
A document that lays down guidelines for safe electrical installation practice. They are issued by the Institution of Electrical Engineers, but do not have any legal force in England and Wales (in Scotland they form part of the Building Regulations, and so are enforceable). Their requirements are followed throughout this book.

Insulation
On flex and cable, this protects users of electrical equipment from touching live conductors.

Junction box
Used on power circuits to connect in spurs, and on lighting circuits to link the circuit cables to each ceiling rose or light fitting and its switch. Also known as joint boxes.

Knockout
Pre-formed weak spot in mounting boxes, designed to be knocked out to admit cables.

Lampholder
An insulated metallic socket into which lamps are plugged.

Lamp
The correct 'trade' term for light bulbs and tubes.

Live
A term that describes the cable or flex core carrying current to a wiring accessory or appliance, or any terminal to which this core is connected. Core insulation is colour-coded for identification; the live core is red in cables, brown in flex.

Loop-in light circuit
Circuit wired by running cable to each ceiling rose in turn. The switch cable is linked directly to the rose it controls.

Luminaire support coupler (LSC)
An ingenious plug-and-socket system used for pendant ceiling lights and wall lights, allowing the light fitting to be simply unplugged for cleaning or maintenance.

Miniature circuit breaker (MCB)
Electromechanical switch which is used instead of circuit fuses in modern consumer units.

Mini-trunking
Surface-mounted PVC channelling with a U-shaped body and snap-on cover, for concealing and protecting cable.

Mounting box
Metal box (for flush fitting) or plastic one (for surface-mounting) over which accessory faceplates are fitted.

Neutral
A term that describes the cable or flex core carrying current back to its source, or any terminal to which this core is connected. Core insulation is colour-coded for identification; the neutral core is black in cable, blue in flex.

One-way switch
Switch that controls a light from one switch position only. It contains two terminals per gang, often marked L1 and L2.

Plateswitch
The 'trade' term for a wall-mounted light switch.

Radial circuit
Power circuit originating at the consumer unit and terminating at the most remote socket outlet, or at an individual appliance.

Residual current device (RCD)
A protective safety device fitted to circuits to detect current leakage which could start a fire or cause an electric shock. Now used in modern consumer units, and to protect users of appliances out of doors.

Ring circuit
Power circuit wired as a continuous loop, both ends being connected to the same terminals in the consumer unit.

Single pole switch
Switch that cuts only the live side of the circuit it controls. Most light switches are of this type.

Socket outlet
A wiring accessory with recessed terminals into which the pins of three-pin plugs fit, allowing appliances to be connected to and disconnected from the mains.

Spur
Cable 'branch line' connected to a house circuit to supply extra lights or sockets.

Switchfuse unit
A small consumer unit containing just one or two fuseways, used to provide extra circuits and fitted alongside the existing fusebox or consumer unit.

Two-way switches
Switches that are used in pairs to allow control of one light from two switch positions. Each gang has three terminals, allowing the switches to be linked by special three-core-and-earth cable. These may be labelled C, L1 and L2, or L1, L2 and L3. The first system is used in the text of this book.

Unit
A measure of the amount of electricity consumed by an appliance or circuit, used for pricing purposes by electricity boards. It is the product of the power consumed (measured in watts) and the time during which it was supplied. One unit is 1 kiloWatt-hour (kWh) – used by, for example, a 100-watt bulb burning for 10 hours.

Volt
The unit of electrical 'pressure' – the potential difference that drives current round a circuit. Usually abbreviated to V. In most British homes main voltage is 240V.

Watt
The unit of power consumed by an appliance or circuit, usually abbreviated to W. It is the product of mains voltage × current drawn (in amps). 1000W = kiloWatt.

INDEX